S0-BOK-348

The Changing Climate of South Texas 1900-2100:
Problems and Prospects
Impacts and Implications

Jim Norwine and Kuruvilla John, editors

CREST-RESSACA
Texas A&M University-Kingsville

2007

Copyright © 2007

All rights reserved.

No part of this book may be reproduced in any form or by any electronic or mechanical means, including information storage and retrieval systems, without written permission from the publisher except by a reviewer who may quote passages in a review.

The Changing Climate of South Texas 1900-2100:
Problems and Prospects, Impacts and Implications
Jim Norwine and Kuruvilla John, editors

Library of Congress Control Number 2007933151

ISBN 978-0-9798426-0-3

Printed by BookMasters, Inc.

Cover art: "Avalanche by Wind" by Alexandre Houge at the University of Arizona Museum of Art

Copy-editing, composition, and layout by Carla Suson

Printed in the United States of America

CONTRIBUTORS

Dr. Kuruvilla John, Associate Professor of Environmental Engineering and Associate Dean in the Frank H. Dotterweich College of Engineering , Texas A&M University-Kingsville

Dr. Jim Norwine, Regents Professor of Geography, Department of Physics and Geosciences, Texas A&M University-Kingsville

Dr. Gerald North, Distinguished Professor, Department of Meteorology, Texas A&M University, College Station

Dr. Robert Harriss, President, Houston Advanced Research Center, The Woodlands, Texas.

Dr. Jaehyung Yu, Assistant Professor of Geography and Geology in the Department of Physics and Geosciences, Texas A&M University-Kingsville

Dr. Claudia Tebaldi, Project Scientist, National Center for Atmospheric Research, Boulder, Colorado

Dr. Ralph Bingham, Professor, Department of Mathematics, and Statistician, Caesar Kleberg Wildlife Research Institute, Texas A&M University-Kingsville

Dr. John W. Tunnell, Jr., Associate Director, Harte Research Scientist, Harte Research Institute for Gulf of Mexico Studies, Director of the Center for Coastal Studies, and Professor of Biology, Texas A&M University-Corpus Christi

Dr. Paul Montagna, Endowed Chair for Ecosystem Studies and Modeling, Harte Research Institute for Gulf of Mexico Studies, Texas A&M University-Corpus Christi

Dr. James C. Gibeaut, Research Associate, the Bureau of Economic Geology, Jackson School of Geosciences, University of Texas at Austin

Dr. Leonard Brennan, Endowed Chair for Quail Research, Caesar Kleberg Wildlife Research Institute and Research Scientist and Professor, Texas A&M University-Kingsville

Dr. Jhumoor Biswas, Department of Environmental Engineering, Frank H. Dotterweich College of Engineering, Texas A&M University-Kingsville

Dr. Venkatesh Uddameri, Associate Professor of Environmental Engineering Frank H. Dotterweich College of Engineering, Texas A&M University-Kingsville

Gomathishankar Parvathinathan, Department of Environmental Engineering, Frank H. Dotterweich College of Engineering, Texas A&M University-Kingsville

Dr. Kim Jones, Associate Professor and Chair of the Department of Environmental Engineering, Frank H. Dotterweich College of Engineering and Director, South Texas Environmental Engineering Institute, Texas A&M University-Kingsville

Irama Wesselman, Department of Environmental Engineering, Frank H. Dotterweich College of Engineering, Texas A&M University-Kingsville

Dr. John Rappole, Research Scientist, Smithsonian Zoological Park Conservation and Research Center, Front Royal, Virginia

Dr. Gene Blacklock, Coastal Bend Bays and Estuaries Program

ACKNOWLEDGEMENTS

This material is based upon work supported by the National Science Foundation under Grant No. HRD-0206259. Any opinions, findings, and conclusions or recommendations expressed in this material are those of the authors and do not necessarily reflect the views of the National Science Foundation.

CREST– RESSACA: Research on Environmental Sustainability of Semi-Arid Coastal Areas

For more information contact:
CREST-RESSACA
Texas A&M University-Kingsville
700 University Blvd., MSC 213
Kingsville, TX 78363
Ph: 361-593-5556   Fax: 361-593-2069

TABLE OF CONTENTS

Prologue: Welcome to the "Anthropocene"? South Texas Climate 2100: Still Fascinating,
Even More Challenging" by Jim Norwine and Kuruvilla John, editors.. 1

1. Introduction by Gerald North 5

2. The Problematic Climate of South Texas 1900-2100 by Jim Norwine,
Robert Harriss, Jaehyung Yu, Claudia Tebaldi, and Ralph Bingham 15

3. South Texas Climate 2100: Coastal Impacts by John W. Tunnell, Jr,
Paul Montagna, and.James C. Gibeaut, ... 57

4. South Texas Climate 2100: Potential Ecological and Wildlife Impacts
by Leonard A. Brennan 79

5. Climate Change Impacts on Regional and Urban Air Quality in South Texas
by Jhumoor Biswas and Kuruvilla John 91

6. Climate Change Impacts on Water Resources in South Texas
by Venkatesh Uddameri and Gomathishankar Parvathinathan.. 109

7. Climate Change for South Texas and Water Resource Impacts: A Specific Focus on
the Agriculture Sector by Kim Jones and Irama Wesselman... 127

8. Apparent Rapid Range Change in South Texas Birds: Response to
Climate Change? by John Rappole, Gene Blacklock, and Jim Norwine...................................... 133

9. South Texas Climate 2100: Reflections, Prospects, Prescriptions
by Robert Harriss... 147

Epilogue by Kuruvilla John and Jim Norwine 153

Index..155

Prologue

Welcome to the "Anthropocene"?[1] South Texas Climate 2100:
Still Fascinating, Even More Challenging

Jim Norwine and Kuruvilla John

"Three things can happen when you pass (rather than run) the football and two of them are bad."
Hall-of-Fame Alabama Crimson Tide football coach Paul "Bear" Bryant.

The Greek philosopher Heraclitus claimed that the only real constant in nature is inconstancy or flux: "…everything flows, nothing stands still...nothing endures but change…you could not step twice into the same river." Things change, but they also remain the same. Heraclitus was actually arguing for an underlying *unity in nature*. One could not step into the same river twice, for example, because "though the waters are always changing, the rivers stay the same."[2]

Change and constancy. In studying South Texas' unforgiving climate (think "death by a thousand cuts"), it becomes all too clear why "the more things change the more they stay the same" is a truism. Like Heraclitus' waters, our climate will change but like his river, it will also retain its fundamental character. This fundamental character of the region is fascinating and not for the faint-hearted. This book is about that seeming paradox and about what it means.

South Texas is a curious place. Most inhabitants and many visitors correctly intuit that there is something very different about the region's physical environment. How can a place so humid, so "sweaty," characterized sometimes by months (most often Septembers) with ten or even twenty inches of rainfall, give rise to such brown landscapes of cactus, mesquite, and rattlesnakes? *The Changing Climate of South Texas 1900 to 2100* begins with an exploration and explanation of the question of how and why South Texas is indeed both wet and dry, a very unusual "desert jungle."

South Texas is classified as a subtropical, subhumid to semiarid type positioned literally and figuratively in-between the moisture-surplus climates to the east and the Chihuahuan Desert to the west. "In between" is the particular key. Just as the region is *subhumid* because it is positioned on the east-west divide between wet and dry regimes, it is also *subtropical* or in between the seasonal climates to the north and the tropical or frost-free types to the south.

Our climate has been described in the literature as a "problem climate" because of its challenge to human and natural ecologies and economies. Above all, its problematic nature stems from extremes in inter-annual variability of rainfall; evapotranspiration (moisture loss) rates during dry periods that are typically three to five times those of precipitation; and, infrequent but significant extreme events such as killing freezes. Alas, our reading of the future suggests that these features will persist.

The reader of *The Changing Climate of South Texas 1900-2100: Problems and Prospects, Impacts and Implications* will discover many uncertainties about the future climate of South Texas. Among these, rainfall is probably the most significant. Although a statistical analysis of climate models suggests that mean annual precipitation could be similar to current levels in 2100, that is by no means certain. Other studies indicate that the subtropics and the American Great Plains are two of the parts of the globe likely to be most moisture-problematic, i.e., seem likely to receive less precipitation than at present. South Texas is located where these two meet. On the other hand, it has also been argued that more frequent downpours associated with more frequent and stronger hurricanes and El Niño events could translate into increased rainfall for South Texas.

The reader will also discover that we face a perhaps surprising number of certainties, or at least near-certainties. Here is a short list of some aspects of our future climate which seem to be very likely:

- South Texas will warm on average through this century, so that by 2100, hard winter freezes are much less common but summer heat waves[*] much more frequent;

---

[*] i.e., multiple days with highs near or above 37.87°C (100ºF)

- Because it will be hotter, even if annual rainfall remains roughly constant or increases a bit, the region will become drier due to increased evapotranspiration rates;
- Our (in)famous variability[†] will probably increase as the climate mutates into one of more prolonged droughts and more extreme rainfall events/periods; and,
- South Texas' character as a "problem climate"[‡] will be exaggerated, with a number of potentially disturbing economic, environmental, and ecological consequences.

As already noted, the existing climate of eastern South Texas (for example Victoria and Corpus Christi) is classified in moisture terms as "subhumid," that of western locations like Laredo is considered "semiarid," while virtually the entire region lies in the thermal zone called "subtropical." It is positioned between the middle latitudes which experience winters and summers and the lower-latitudes or tropics, which are winterless. Now to anticipate the future, imagine picking up the entire region and moving it a hundred or so miles west, i.e., towards the Chihuahuan Desert, and a similar distance south. And, because of rising sea levels, one should expect the migration and/or loss of coastal barrier island and wetland environments and the intrusion of additional salt water into crucial groundwater supplies. Given the warming and drying suggested by leading climate models, this seems to roughly but accurately visualize how our climate and its effects will shift over the coming one hundred years.

So what? That is what this book is about. South Texas will surely retain its harsh beauty but it is unlikely to become any more benign. The future climate described here will only exacerbate the serious demographic and economic and environmental challenges the region faces.[3]

Nobel-Prize recipient (chemistry) Paul Crutzen recently characterized ours as a new, human-dominated geological epoch, the "Anthropocene:" "It seems appropriate to assign the term "Anthropocene" to the present…human-dominated geological epoch, supplementing the Holocene, the warm period of the past ten to twelve millennia. The Anthropocene could be said to have started in the latter part of the eighteenth century, when analyses of air trapped in polar ice showed the beginning of growing global concentrations of carbon dioxide and methane. Unless there is a global catastrophe such as a meteorite impact, a world war, or a pandemic, mankind will remain a major environmental force for many millennia. A daunting task lies ahead for scientists and engineers to guide society toward environmentally sustainable management during the Anthropocene."[1]

The Changing Climate of South Texas 1900- 2100: Problems and Prospects, Impacts and Implications is our attempt to respond responsibly to Dr. Crutzen's "daunting task" challenge. The professional lives of the contributors have revolved around the assumption that knowledge is superior to ignorance. In this book, we present state-of-the-science knowledge concerning both our future climate and its most likely impacts on and implications for human and natural ecologies and economies. The chapters have been written by top-of-their-field scientists and engineers at institutions such as the National Center for Atmospheric Research, the Houston Advanced Research Center, Texas A&M University-Corpus Christi's Harte Research Center, Texas A&M University-Kingsville, and Caesar Kleberg Wildlife Research Institute. This book is our way to share the best current knowledge with the citizens, leaders, teachers, and students of an adopted home we have come to love. That is our responsibility as scholars, and we are honored to have endeavored to fulfill that duty.

More than that, we and all living South Texans share an obligation to the Texans of 2100 and beyond. It is to them that we respectfully dedicate this book.

[†] e.g., years of ten inches followed by years of fifty inches of precipitation
[‡] i.e., a regime inherently challenging to successful use by people and many other organisms

Literature Cited

[1]Crutzen, Paul. Human Impact on Climate Has Made This the 'Anthropocene' Age. *New Perspectives Quarterly*, 22 (2) (Spring 2005). http://www.digitalnpq.org/archive/2005_spring/03_crutzen.html.

[2]Graham, Daniel W. Heraclitus. The Internet Encyclopedia of Philosophy, http://www.iep.utm.edu/h/heraclit.htm (November 16, 2006).

[3]It should be noted that the future-climate simulations and characterizations described in the chapter on the climate of South Texas 1900-2100, and utilized in the three following chapters on likely impacts and implications, were made prior to the most recent IPCC Intergovernmental Panel on Climate Change (IPCC) reports in February and March 2007. Those latest findings are addressed in the Introduction by Dr. Gerald North.

1

Introduction

Gerald R. North

This is a book about the climate of South Texas, its past, its present, and its future as well as impacts of future changes on the region. Global climate is changing and the climate of South Texas is changing along with it. Why is global climate changing and how is South Texas to be affected by it? What measures might to be taken to minimize the negative consequences, if any?

Global climate change has surfaced as a major scientific activity over the last quarter century. Before that, it was the haven for a handful of geographers and meteorologists around the world – most countries could claim a few. Data were gathered and climatologies of different regions were compiled. These were useful in many applications from water resource planning to insurance and architecture. But climate research began in earnest at the international level in the 1970s, and activity has accelerated ever since. A new discipline emerged, building on experience in the acquisition and interpretation of data; satellite observations; and computer modeling used in weather forecasting and engineering. In a very short time, it has matured to a level of being capable of supplying answers to questions that had earlier been thought to be impossible.

The globe is warming because of the activities of man beginning with the industrial revolution in the mid-1700s. We have been pumping carbon dioxide into the atmosphere at rates faster than the system can absorb it and hence about half of what we are injecting is remaining there for centuries. This so-called greenhouse gas (along with some others, we are responsible for as well) puts a layer of gas overhead that allows sunlight to pass right through but absorbs infrared radiation. Just as in a greenhouse, the layer (glass panes of the roof) of greenhouse gas absorbs the infrared and finds itself a bit warmer than before. Now we (and the potted plants) get a double whammy: 1) the sunlight warming our rosy cheeks, 2) the warm layer of air radiating infrared rays down on us (like the old steam radiator used to warm our backsides) and as the warmed glass panes of the greenhouse roof radiating down on the potted plants below. The analogy is not perfect but it will do.

As we increase the concentration of the greenhouse gases we proceed to warm the Earth's surface a little more every year. There are broad implications. When the energy balance of the Earth changes even a little, the circulation patterns of the atmosphere and oceans will also change. Evaporation and precipitation patterns will change with winners and losers around the planet. Members of threatened ecosystems will scramble for safety with Darwin looking over their shoulders. The heated oceans will expand, raising sea level, again winners and losers. Mountain glaciers are melting at rates not exceeded for thousands of years. As they melt, the sea surface rises due to the inflow fresh melt water, greater storm surges following.

The Nature of Climate Research

In climate studies we don't get very far without numbers. This is a science, not stamp collecting. We have to sort the observational information into forms that make sense and are in accord with the laws of physics, biology, etc. We cannot be satisfied with tables of data and attractive maps (although these are often very useful), but instead we demand understanding of the climate system sufficient to make useful predictions (at least in a probabilistic sense) of what is going to happen to the system if we perturb it in some way. The basic question posed is, what happens to the system if there is effectively an exponentially increasing concentration of greenhouse gases in the atmosphere, doubling about every seventy years?

To achieve this understanding, we make simulation models that employ our knowledge of physics, chemistry, biology, numerical analysis and the wisdom gained from observations. These models can be pictured as a covering of the planet by a grid of cubical cells (see Figure 1). The current models make use of an array of cells that on the ground are squares of about one hundred and ninety kilometers (one hundred and twenty miles) on a side. If there are twenty boxes stacked in the vertical, this amounts to about a quarter of a million boxes for the atmosphere. One must keep track of about ten variables (temperature, moisture, pressure, wind components, etc,), bringing the total size of the number of variables to several million. A comparable number goes for the ocean and land surfaces. This quickly becomes a supercomputer problem if we just evaluate these millions of quantities every ten minutes or so of simulation time. Remember, we always need to run several hundred years of simulation time (ten million steps). Just evaluating the variables means 10^{13} (ten million-million) calculations. But there is more: we have to adjust the values in the cells from one time step to another by implementing the laws of physics, chemistry, biology, etc. For example, if we find that the air in a cell has a temperature warmer than that in neighboring boxes at the same level, the program has to let it rise into the cells above, just after this action there will need to be a horizontal flow into the vacuum left behind. Water is moving around, clouds are forming, rain is falling, rivers are running, water is evaporating from the ocean surface, making it more saline (more dense), etc. On today's supercomputers, the simulation of a century's climate takes several months of computer (wall-clock) time. There are about twenty of these global climate models operating more or less independently of one another around the world. Model results differ slightly from one another. These differences provide one (imperfect) way of estimating our uncertainty in the forecast.

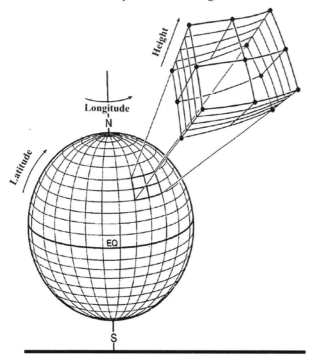

Figure 1. Schematic of a grid used in global climate modeling. The exploded section denotes the vertically distributed boxes that are stacked above the surface.

Once we have the model running, we can commence to perform experiments within its artificial climate system. For instance, we can ask what happens if the solar brightness is increased by 1%. The answer is that the global average temperature will go up by several degrees Celsius (1.8 times that to get degrees Fahrenheit). We can conduct and use the model for other very practical applications. For example, we can ask what happens to the atmospheric circulation if we increase the sea surface temperatures in a patch of the Equatorial Pacific near the International Date Line (180^0 W). This is an artificial El Nino and the answer is that Texas will have a wetter winter. The model works in cases like this as has been shown in thousands of such experiments where we have the next season's observations to check the results. Note that we cannot predict which day it will rain in Texas, but we can say with some confidence that the season will be a wet one, due to the shift in location of the storm tracks over the winter.

In the climate change problem, there are differences in the predictions from one model to another. In fact, there can be as much as a plus or minus 50% spread in global average temperature change across the results for a given scenario over the next century. Much of the uncertainty is because we cannot pin down the uncertainty in the feedback mechanisms (internal amplifiers and deflators) operating in the system. The basic flow patterns, etc., are pretty similar from one model to another, but the algorithms utilized in the feedback mechanisms are very tricky and different modeling groups have their own individual ways of implementing them. There will always be some uncertainty; it is likely to diminish over time, but it will never be eliminated completely.

Climate Drivers

What external drivers influence the global climate? The climate system derives all of its energy from the sun. The sun's brightness, the Earth's orbital parameters, its surface reflectivity, and the atmosphere's composition essentially determine the global climate. A simple back-of-the-envelope calculation shows that the Earth with no atmosphere (and its present reflectivity to sunlight) would yield an average temperature below freezing – probably cold enough to ice over. This is not what actually happens. Small amounts of water vapor and trace amounts of other greenhouse gases inhabit the space above the surface and these gases intercept the upwelling infrared radiation from the surface. The greenhouse gases do their job and warm the surface. The bottom line is that there is a greenhouse effect and we couldn't live without it. The presence of water vapor and a host of other mechanisms brought about by it (e.g., clouds) are enough to raise the global average temperature up to about 14°C (57°F). Even the simplest climate models simulate this very well.

Before proceeding to an enumeration of the drivers of climate change, it is well to discuss feedback mechanisms in the system. A simple explanation of the greenhouse was given in an earlier section. But there are internal mechanisms that can amplify or deflate the response of the system to an external perturbation (Held and Soden 2000). Let's look at just one of these in some detail to illustrate how it can happen. After an initial perturbation (say, increased solar brightness), more water vapor enters the air column evaporating from the warmer, wet surface. The water vapor mixes upwards a bit higher than before in the space above the surface where the surrounding air is cooler. This cooler water vapor layer cannot radiate as much to space as it did at its previous warmer level. But the sunlight warming the surface and the whole air column has increased slightly. This excess heating from the sunlight will warm the whole column until the temperature of the water vapor at its new height (and it subsequent radiation rate to space) is warm enough to match the incoming solar heating rate. The column of air (to a good approximation) changes its whole profile rigidly.[*] So warming the air one degree at a few kilometers above the ground will cause it to warm about the same amount throughout the column including the surface. Once this is achieved equilibrium will be restored with the result that the surface will be warmer. This is a long-winded explanation of both the water vapor greenhouse effect (the double whammy) and the so-called water vapor feedback mechanism.[†]

The water vapor feedback process just discussed leads to an amplification of roughly 100% in the response to virtually all the drivers we will discuss (Held and Soden 2000). It works both ways. If a driver tends to cool the climate, the feedback will diminish the response by 50%. There are other feedbacks in the system, both positive (amplifiers) and negative (deflators). The details of including feedbacks varies from one model to another. Fortunately, they all agree on the largest of them all, the water vapor feedback.

Besides the sun's variation in brightness, there are several other drivers of climate change of interest in the present context. One is the dust veil brought about by major volcanic eruptions. These events spew large amounts of particles into the stratosphere.[‡] The tiny particles are mostly made up of sulfur compounds dissolved in water droplets that reflect sunlight back to space, not allowing it to enter (and warm) the climate system below. The tiny particles (called aerosols) have fall speeds so slow they can remain in the stratosphere for years before being removed by coagulation and atmospheric circulation mechanisms (Hamill, et al. 1997). We can see the signature of the volcanic events in the Earth's temperature record. A discernable cooling of a fraction of a degree Celsius follows every major eruption from Tambora to Mt. Pinatubo. These events provide comfort to climate scientists that external perturbations can cause climate change in conformity with their basic theory. The coolings due to volcanic events are not sufficient data to pin down the sensitivity of the climate to radiation imbalances, because they are short pulses (in the long term sense), and the upper ocean has something to say about the magnitude and time evolution of the global response. Nevertheless, there is a reassuring consistency that the cool notches are there.

Another important driver is the aerosol loading of the atmosphere by natural and anthropogenic processes. Natural processes include the wind's lofting of natural debris due to decaying biological matter such as fallen leaves. Also sea spray leaves behind tiny salt particles. Wind blown soil and mineral matter also contribute. Natural fires emit smoke particles that include many different chemical species. Man produces aerosols by burning fuels and by clearing of forested areas. Most aerosols reflect sunlight back to space like the volcanic ones in the stratosphere, leading to a cooling of the surface climate, but some anthropogenic aerosols contain black carbon and these tend to absorb solar radiation locally and warm the surrounding air. The current data suggest that the net effect is to cool the planet due to the screening out of sunlight. Finally, anthropogenic aerosols can modify clouds with effects that are largely unknown at present, but the evidence favors their leading to a cooling.

---

[*] This rigidity is disputed by some, and its possible 'non-rigidity' might be yet another feedback called lapse rate feedback.
[†] The greenhouse roof thickens and raises of to higher [and cooler] elevations because of the water vapor's increase in concentration with temperature.
[‡] the atmospheric layers above where the jet planes fly – about ten kilometers or 30,000 feet

The final driver is the change in chemical composition of the atmosphere through increasing greenhouse gases such as carbon dioxide, methane, nitrous oxide, and chlorofluorocarbons. If these concentrations are increased, they raise the elevation of emission to space, first causing the radiation to space to decrease because they are emitting from a cooler height, but now the solar warming will exceed the cooling and this will cause the whole column of air to warm, including the surface. Next the water vapor feedback will amplify the warming because of its own greenhouse effect's increase. Other feedback mechanisms in the system will also come into play. There are several more, and we need not elaborate them here. They also tend to amplify the response, but not as much as water vapor.

I have introduced four drivers that are of direct interest to current climate change problems. There are others that operate on much slower time scales such as the changes in the Earth's orbital parameters (periods of 100, 41, and 22 thousands of years). These cycles in solar energy distribution through the seasons and over the latitudes explain the timing of the glaciations of the last few million years. Another is the drifting of the continents. The continental configurations change on time scales of millions of years and can radically alter the seasonal cycle at places on the planet, initiating and destroying ice sheets depending on what's happening at the poles (land, no land, or some land). There are also feedback mechanisms that may operate on long time scales that we do not fully understand, such as the regulation of carbon dioxide via mountain building/erosion cycle (million year time scale). Greenhouse gases also can be freed from the sea floor by disrupting deposits of them through hot lava flows, for example (thousand year time scales). On the few thousand years' time scale or possibly less, the expansion of ice sheets seems to disrupt, probably through biological pathways, the carbon cycle causing carbon dioxide and methane to remove themselves from the atmosphere. This greenhouse amplifier, and its reverse on the ice-sheet decay side, seems to be essential in the growth of the ice sheets during glacial/interglacial cycles.

Scientific Assessments

All this is rather bewildering to the policymaker or layman wanting to know what is going on and what could/should be done. The degree of complication of the climate system is comparable to but not quite as bad as that of the inner workings of the human body. When we are sick, we ask around and choose a doctor for help. We have to rely on expert help in the matter. It is often wise to get a second opinion. If it is an epidemic we seek expertise on a greater scale, say the Center for Disease Control. Our local doctor may not know the solution. We also follow the newspapers for stories about new cures and the assessments of their effectiveness. This points the way to the scientific assessment process.

There are several ways of conducting a scientific assessment for the climate problem. One is via the U.S. National Academy of Sciences (NAS). In this case, typically a committee is formed to address a specific scientific question and the members are carefully chosen so as to be knowledgeable but have no conflict of interest, etc. The report is to be based on the peer-reviewed scientific literature. Then, the report itself is peer-reviewed before its release to the public. In the case of global climate change, it is essential to obtain international acceptance of the assessment and so we turn to an international body: the United Nations in collaboration with the World Meteorological Organization.[§] These groups then convene the Intergovernmental Panel on Climate Change (IPCC). The IPCC reports can be downloaded at http://www.ipcc.ch.

The IPCC was first formed in the late 1980s when global climate change was recognized to be a potential threat. The IPCC is charged with issuing a report on the state of the art of climate research approximately every five years. Reports were issued in 1990, 1995, 2001, and most recently 2007. More than a hundred countries participate. These reports come from three working groups: Working Group I reports on the physical science, Working Group II reports on the impacts of the science, and Working Group III reports on the means of dealing with any perceived problems. Each Working Group issues its findings in two parts, first a Summary for Policy Makers (about twenty-five pages) and then a detailed document of the order of a thousand pages.

The detailed reports consist of chapters, each of which has multiple authors from many different countries. Diversity of authorship is paramount. Drafts of the chapters based upon the peer-reviewed literature are sent out to anonymous reviewers and the comments and criticisms are collected and taken into account. The next draft is made available to the public for comments. In all, tens of thousands of comments come in and are dealt with. Finally, a committee of scientists drafts the Summaries for Policy Makers in collaboration with governmental representatives from the participating countries. The result is an assessment of the state of the art with some (usually conservative) political tuning of the words. All things considered these are probably the most thoroughly vetted scientific assessments in the history of science.

[§] The venerable institution has successfully collected and coordinated weather observations from around the world for day-to-day forecasting by local weather services for many decades.

Findings of the 2001 IPCC Report received strong statements of endorsement by the American Geophysical Union, the American Meteorological Society, and the American Association for the Advancement of Science. In addition, the U.S. National Academy of Sciences has released several reports in agreement with the findings of the report.

Over the several reports, there has been a convergence of the statements toward more certainty in many respects. First, the degree of confidence in our ability to understand climate change has increased from one report to the next. Second, the certainty with which we can assert that global warming has occurred over the last century and even over the last several centuries has increased. The reports conclude with ever more confidence that the drivers of climate change (greenhouse gases, volcanic aerosols, anthropogenic aerosols, solar variability, land surface changes) are better understood especially over recent decades (the satellite era). The attribution of the warming to human behavior has sharpened with each of the succeeding reports to the point that it is given a nine out of ten chance of being true (see Figure 2).

So, do assessments like that of the IPCC tell us the truth? We cannot ask that assessments get us to the truth. They can only tell us with some degree of confidence what the science community is saying at this time, based on its own internal controls, mainly peer reviewing of papers and peer reviewing of proposals for financial support of research. Even in the final statement of the 2007 report, there is some wiggle room in the statement that there is a 10% chance that they have it wrong.

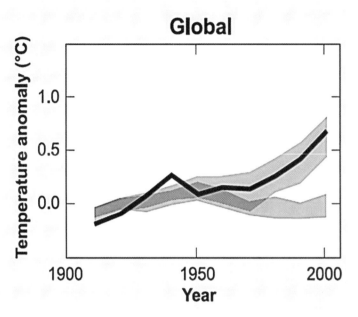

Figure 2. Global average temperatures: Solid black line indicates observations; Pink shaded area represents the 95% confidence band when all drivers are included in climate model simulations. Blue shaded area indicates the same confidence band if greenhouse gases and anthropogenic aerosols are omitted in the simulation. (IPCC 2007 Working Group I Summary for Policy Makers)

Future Climates in the World and in Texas

Consider the future global climate and especially that of South Texas. The 2007 IPCC Report (often referred to as Assessment Report Four or simply AR4) provides us with state of the art assessments of what is known about the climate system and its future. The major conclusions of the AR4 are easily found at http://www.ipcc.ch. The main findings are that the Earth has warmed some three quarters of a degree Celsius (1.25°F) over the last century and that most of this is of human origin (see Figure 3). There will be some shifting polewards in mid-latitude weather patterns especially the latitude of the storm belts (Yin 2005; Bengtsson et al. 2006). Sea level has been rising and it will continue to rise and accelerate. Snow cover is decreasing, along with sea ice and mountain glaciers. Forecasts of future climate are presented based on scenarios proposed by economists. Of course, the details depend on the scenarios one uses for input of greenhouse gases and other factors over the coming century. Many scenarios are discussed in the report, but the one of most interest in the present context is one in which the carbon dioxide concentration levels at about mid-century (scenario B1FI). Some warming will continue after that, but the global climate toward the end of the century based on this scenario is the one we shall consider.

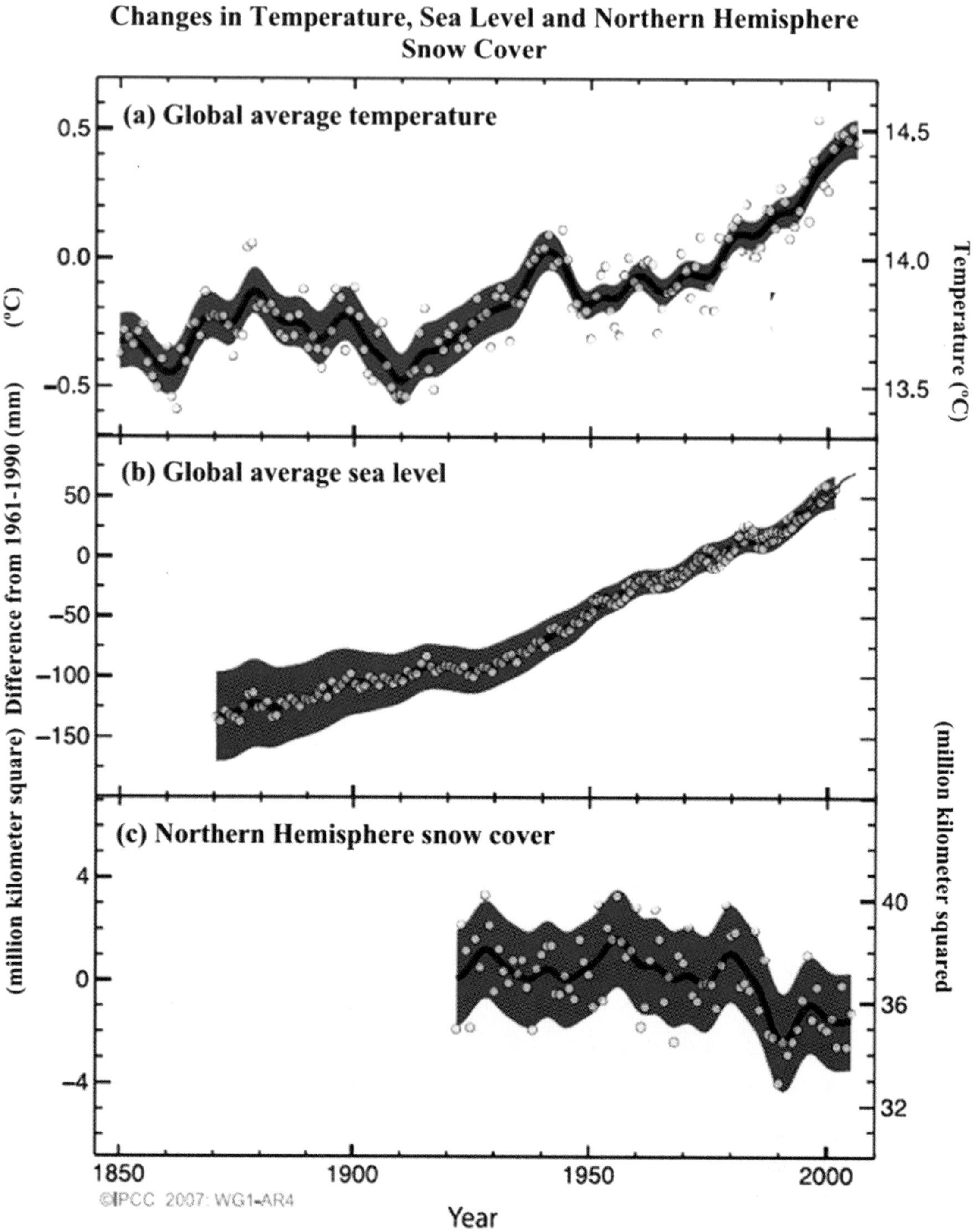

Changes in Temperature, Sea Level and Northern Hemisphere
Snow Cover

Figure 3. Climate of the last century and a half. Darkened areas indicate the uncertainty (likelihood of 95%) in the estimations. Individual dots represent annual averages. The black solid line represents a ten-year running average. (IPCC 2007 Working Group I Summary for Policy Makers, www-as.harvard.edu/chemistry/trop/img/model_grid.png)

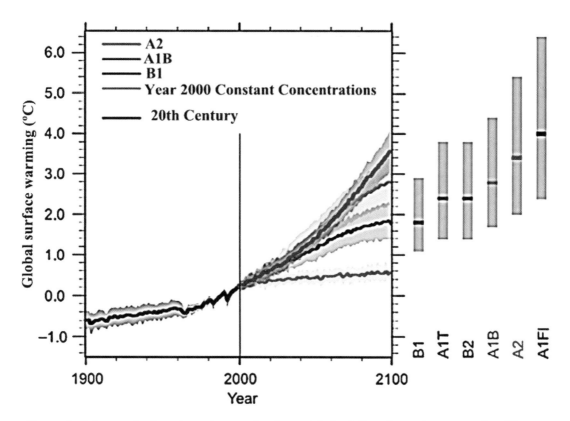

Figure 4. Future projections based upon climate model simulations for various scenarios. The orange line is the solution for constant greenhouse gases from the year 2000. Scenario A1FI is a business as usual scenario, while B1 is a case where the emissions are leveled at 2050. (IPCC 2007 Working Group I Summary for Policy Makers)

The likelihood is for a warmer South Texas by approximately the same amount as the global average temperature. Latitudes to the north of South Texas will warm a bit more than the global average, those to the south a bit less, but a good rule of thumb is that South Texas will warm at about the same rate at the global average.

The global average temperature is expected to increase about 2.0°C (3.6°F) between now and the end of the century, so we can take this to be the result for South Texas. Of special interest is the future water situation in South Texas. Precipitation is not so robust a variable to predict as large-area averaged temperatures. One intuitive result about global warming is that the global hydrological cycle will intensify: while temperatures rise, at least there will be more rain. This is true on a global basis, but not nearly as big an effect as was once thought. If global precipitation increased proportionally as the vapor pressure of water increases we could expect about 7% per degree Celsius increase in precipitation globally. Instead the models suggest only a tiny fraction (about 1/20) of this increase over the next hundred years (Held and Soden 2006).

The spread of predictions across different models is greater for precipitation. Precipitation depends on weather patterns (mid-latitude storm tracks, etc.), which are more subtle to forecast than mere large scale temperature averages. In recent years there have been many studies reaching the conclusion that the mid-latitude storm tracks that currently cross the United States oscillating south in the winter, then receding into Canada in summer will undergo a gradual overall shift polewards. This shift will have profound consequences for moisture in South Texas.

First recall that South Texas gets rain during the winter as fronts cross the area one after another. It is particularly stormy during late spring and early fall. The last front usually passes through in June and the first of the new fall season comes in September. During the summer months there are no fronts, and we experience a tropical climate. The descending branch of the Hadley cell is over our heads and the air column is filled with sinking air (Frierson 2006). Sinking air is anathema to precipitation. The descending branch of the Hadley Cell is home to most of the world's desserts. Sure, there is some rain due to afternoon thunderstorms and near the coast we get some sea breeze rain. But those good soaking rains filling aquifers with fresh water and generating runoff above the surface into our streams will be less frequent. Basically as the storm track recedes to the north, we will have a longer tropical summer with the associated descending air that inhibits precipitation.

What about the global hydrological cycle increases? According to the model simulations (Held and Soden 2006) the increased evaporation does fill the atmospheric boundary layer with moisture but there is a lack of lifting mechanisms to convert the humidity into precipitation. Instead the sinking air in the region causes the humid air to be diverging and flowing out of the region rather than raining in place.

Another recent finding is that the low frequency variability (periods of several years to a decade) in the southwestern part of the United States will increase compared to higher frequency (periods shorter than a year) behavior (Seager et al. 2007). Several studies have shown that most multiyear droughts in the Great Plains and Texas have been related to persistent patches of warm sea surface temperatures in the Pacific Ocean (Schubert et al. 2004). Simulations in many of the AR4 models show more long periods of severe drought and extreme wetness as the climate evolves over the century. The eastern part of Texas and the entire eastern (and especially the northeastern) U.S. should enjoy more water and all of its associated benefits. The study by Seager et al. (2007) shows the trend is already evident in last part of the Twentieth Century. The simulations indicate that the drought of the 1950s (the 'drought of record' used by hydrologists for water resource planning), will be the norm in the southwestern U.S. late in the century.

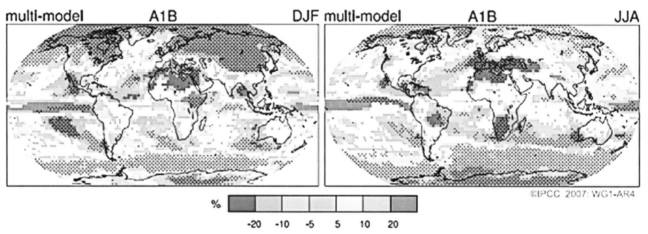

Figure 5. Climate model simulations for precipitation results at the end of the century. White areas are those for which there is insufficient unanimity to indicate a change. Note that for this scenario there is much less precipitation in winter for South Texas. (IPCC 2007 Working Group I Summary for Policy Makers)

As we consider the consequences of this forecast, which has about a two-thirds chance of occurring (my odds), we realize that there will be changes in South Texas. For one, the rivers of South Texas will have an even more difficult time making it to the Gulf Coast. This will have profound influences on the estuaries along the Texas coast. With less and even intermittent flow of fresh water into the estuaries, this will have dire consequences for the ecological systems in those habitats.

It is a time for Texans and especially planners to become much attentive to the field of climate and global change research. We can expect the models to be better in time for the Fifth Report of the IPCC due in 2012. It should inform us more about the frequency and intensity of future hurricanes, and El Ninos. In addition, it should tell us more about the chemical and biological changes that are taking place in the Earth system (for example, acidification of the oceans, extinction of species, etc.). Hydrology should be more believable in the next report as well. So, let's not be left behind in the planning process. We need not jump to alarmist proportions, just be prudent: look at the facts weigh them, and take responsible action accordingly.

Literature Cited

Andreadis, K. M. and D. P. Lettenmaier. 2006. Trends in 20th Century Drought over the Continental United States. 33:, doi:10.1029/2006GL025711.

Bengtsson, L., K. I. Hodges, and E. Roeckner. 2006. Storm Tracks and Climate Change. *Journal of Climatology* 19:3518-3543.

Frierson, D. M. W. 2006. Robust Increases in Mid-latitude Static Stability in Simulations of Global Warming. *Geophysical Research Letters* 33:L24816, doi:1029/2006GLO27504.

Hamill, P., E. J. Jensen, P. B. Russell, and J. J. Bauman. 1997. The Life Cycle of Stratospheric Aerosol Particles. *Bulletin of American Meteorological Society*. 78:1395-1410.

Held, I. M., and B. J. Soden. 2000. Water Vapor Feedback and Global Warming. *Annual Rev. Energy Environ.* 25:441-475.

Held, I. M. and B. J. Soden. 2006. Robust Responses of the Hydrological Cycle to Global Warming. *Journal of Climatology* 19: 5686-5699.

Seager, R., M. Ting, I. M. Held, Y. Kushnir, J. Lu, G. Vecchi, H. P. Huang, N. Harnik, A. Leetmaa, N. C. Lau, C. Li, J. Velez, and N. Naik. 2007. Model Projections of an Imminent Transition to a More Arid Climate in Southwestern North America. *Science*. (in press).

Schubert, S. D., M. J. Suarez, P. J. Pegion, R. D. Koster, and J.T. Bacmeister. 2004. Causes of Long-Term Drought in the U.S. Great Plains. *Journal of Climatology* 17:485-503.

Yin, J. H. 2005. A Consistent Poleward Shift of the Storm tracks in Simulations of 21st Century Climate, *Geophysical Research Letters* 32:L18701, doi:10.1029/2005GL023684.

2

The Problematic Climate of South Texas 1900-2100

Jim Norwine, Robert Harriss, Jaehyung Yu, Claudia Tebaldi, and Ralph Bingham

The existing climate of South Texas is fascinating but problematic. For example, it is "wet" due to advection from the nearby Gulf of Mexico, with mean atmospheric humidity levels exceedings every other location in the remainder of conterminous USA excepting southern Florida. But it is also "dry" because mean annual potential evapotranspiration values typically exceed precipitation by two to five times. In this chapter, the regional climatic patterns of the immediate past, i.e. the twentieth century, are first surveyed. It is found that mean annual regional precipitation tended to increase slightly during the century but that mean annual temperature values revealed no clear local global warming signal, although values exhibited a marked increase after about 1985.

Next, the near- to medium-term future is addressed by means of National Center for Atmospheric Research (NCAR) computer-model simulations of the climate of the twenty-first century (2025, 2050, and 2100). Made using model "middle-of-the-road" assumptions, these projections seemed appropriate given recent reports of very significant and mainly negative effects attendant to global warming of about +2 to 3°C (3.6 to 5.4°F) during the twenty-first century (Jha 2006). The results indicate that the climate of South Texas is likely to be even more problematic in the year 2100 than it is at present, due to projected annual rainfall averages near those of the present coupled with much higher mean annual temperatures (about +3 to 4°C or 5.4 to 7.2°F), as well as longer dry spells and more intense precipitation episodes.

Background: Climate Defined

What is climate? Climate is the state of the atmosphere at some place or over some area as measured over very long periods of time by variables like temperature and precipitation. The key phrase is "long periods of time." This is what separates climate from weather, which of course means atmospheric states over short time-periods like days or hours or even a given instant. Like weather, climate's normal state is inconstancy but, unlike weather, it usually changes slowly, over time-spans of centuries, millennia and even millions of years. Because humans are not around long enough to personally witness most of the climate change, it is difficult to accept that climate change as real, but it is. One million years ago, during the chilly Pleistocene Ice Age when ice covered about 30% of Earth's surface, the South Texas climate was probably not unlike that of today's Green Bay, Wisconsin, while even deeper into the past, during a warmer period around thirty-five million years ago, it appears to have been something like that of present-day Vera Cruz, Mexico.

Climate Is Important

Climate <u>is</u> important. In fact, from a human perspective, climate almost certainly constitutes the single most important element of Earth's physical environment. There are many aspects of the planet's physical geography which exert an influence on people, including geology, soils, floral and fauna, and hydrology. However, the reason climate is preeminent is that it not only affects us directly but also indirectly. It is a key driver of the other physical elements. The geology of the three main areas of tropical rainforest climate--the Amazon Basin, Central Africa, and Southeast Asia--could hardly be more dissimilar, yet because of their shared tropIcal rainforest climate, all three regions share the same red lateritic soils, among the most agriculturally inhospitable on our planet.

It is not necessary to subscribe to climate determinism in order to appreciate the geographical good fortune of a country like the United States. The USA is one of the six largest countries on Earth but, unlike Russia, Canada, Brazil, and Australia, its location is almost entirely in the middle-latitudes. (China shares this advantage.) So what? Imagine the United States absent its agricultural heartland. The corn and wheat belts, the world's richest, most productive and most important farming region, exist because of a combination of generally adequate moisture, where the dry west meets the wet east, and long, warm growing seasons, in addition to rich glacial soils. Because the United States is the world's leading grain exporter, any significant shift or decline of this American agricultural heartland due to climate change would pose a serious threat to people everywhere but most especially to those located in poor regions and nations.

Climate Does Not Determine But It Does Influence Humanity

The impact of weather on our lives is often all too obvious. Hurricane Katrina is an exceptionally dramatic example. What is not so obvious is that climate and climatic change affect people every bit as much as weather and weather change do, although more slowly and incrementally. Perhaps just three among many possible examples will make the point:

- A small but thriving Viking community had been established in southern Greenland around the last turn of a millennium, 1,000 CE, during a relatively warm period. That colony completely disappeared because all its members died of cold during the so-called Little Ice Age of 1300 to 1900 CE, a time during which mean temperatures dropped by about 0.5 to 1.0°C (0.9 to 1.8°F).

- Sometime take a few minutes to examine a map of the American interstate highway system. In the east and the mid-west and along the far Pacific coast, the "I" highways look like spaghetti or a mass of squirming worms, running every which way. But in the interior west, there are far fewer interstate highways and those which are there tend mainly to east-west corridors linking the densely populated sections of the country. Most of the west remains relatively underpopulated by humans, as it has been even prior to the arrival of European invaders. Why is this so? The west, dominated by a blocking ridge of high pressure, is dry. Other than the Pacific Northwest, the existing climates of the west are almost entirely either semi-arid steppe or arid desert. Most of the many large cities in the southwest such as El Paso, Phoenix, Tucson, San Diego, and Los Angeles are living on borrowed time, or at least borrowed water, i.e., water which has been "liberated" from wetter areas and transported hundreds of miles, or else "fossil water" pumped out of the ground which cannot naturally be replaced for centuries or even millennia. Contemplate for just a moment the reality that the average yearly rainfall of Los Angeles is at 375 millimeters (14.8 inches) about one-half that of South Texas, a region more noted for mesquite and sage than bubbling brooks, and then reflect on what the real or actual natural carrying capacity of the Los Angles Basin is compared to its present population of fifteen million or so.

- There is one final proof that climate and climate change have affected people. Sixty-five million years ago, dinosaurs had ruled the planet for one hundred and fifty million years. (For comparison, recall that, while *Homo Habilis* figured out tool-making two million years ago, they hardly reigned supreme. *Homo Sapiens Sapiens* first started wearing skins against winter's chill only about seventy thousand years ago. Humans invented agriculture and began to settle down around ten thousand years ago; figured out writing a mere four or five millennia ago; and Copernicus started the Age of Science by demonstrating that Earth orbits the Sun just five hundred years ago.

Humanity's rule during Earth's long history is very short.) Sixty-five million years ago, a chunk of "space rock" plummeted through Earth's atmosphere and struck the northern coast of present-day Yucatan. It created a firestorm but more significantly blasted a pall of debris into the stratosphere which shielded and cooled the planet for at least many months. This was the genesis of the famous "extinction event" which at once ended the Age of Dinosaurs and created an opening for mammals, which up to that point been the size of badgers or smaller. Humanity's eventual domination, far shorter but otherwise not unlike that of the dinosaurs, would never have been possible except for this single sudden climatic change.

The Region: South Texas

This chapter is a kind of case-study. As the world enters what is almost certainly a prolonged period of warming, an examination of one specific and particularly climate-vulnerable region might serve as a benchmark against which similarly climate-sensitive regions may be studied. The region studied here is that part of southern Texas locally known as South Texas.

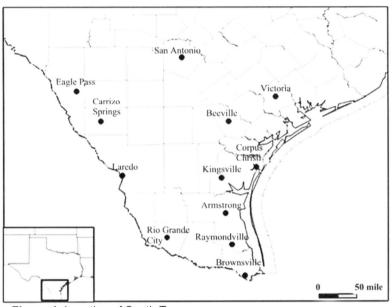

Figure 1. Location of South Texas

What exactly is meant by "South Texas?" To qualify as a region, an area must have a defining character, i.e., exhibit one or more characteristics which set it apart from neighboring regions. Such qualities may be features of physical geography like topography or climate, or they may belong to the realm of human geography; economic or political or religious aspects, for example. It would not be too much of an overstatement to say that regions have a kind of soul or spirit which mere areas lack.

South Texas is a region, one whose distinctive defining nature is the product of an unusual mixture of physical environment and culture. Half of the story is its odd climate and the other half has to do with the region's location and history and culture,

Just where and what is this region? "South Texas" consists of an area of nearly 80,000 square kilometers (50,000 miles^2) bordered to the west by the Big Bend of the Rio Grande and Pecos Rivers; to the north by the Edwards Plateau and its southern edge, the Balcones Escarpment; to the south by the Rio Grande; and, to the east by the Gulf of Mexico. In reality, those limits, especially those to the north and east, are subject to debate.

Flat to gently rolling, physiographically South Texas is the southernmost section of the Gulf-Atlantic Coastal Plain which stretches from eastern Mexico to New York City. Biologically the northern part of the Tamaulipan Biotic Province, the present-day "natural vegetation" in fact is not very natural but has been seriously anthropogenically modified by clearing, reservoir creation, paving and building and, above all, overgrazing.[1] Now largely thorn-scrub "brushland" intermixed with grasses and xerophytes like cacti and yucca, prior to the overgrazing which following European colonization the landscape was probably closer to true subtropical steppe, i.e., a vegetative cover of tall perennial grasses.

The core or heart of South Texas remains the "Wild Horse Desert" or "Mustang Plains," that disputed territory between the Nueces and Rio Grande Rivers claimed by both Texas and Mexico following Texas independence. While commercial agriculture is practiced along the eastern (non-irrigated grain sorghum and cotton) and southern margins (irrigated sugar cane, citrus and vegetables), most of the central and western parts are primarily used for cattle grazing and deer hunting. It is possible that commercial agriculture in both eastern and southern South Texas will be threatened by

---

[1] Senior author's aside: If some time you are fortunate enough to visit Texas A&M University-Kingsville, take a look around as you endeavor to try to find a few "native South Texan" species among the introduced carpet grass, palms, oleanders, bouganvillas, oaks, and even mesquites, which only became ubiquitous following the spread of cattle.

climatic deterioration associated with greenhouse warming by the latter part of this century. (As noted, irrigated farmland in the Lower Rio Grande Valley is already in decline.)

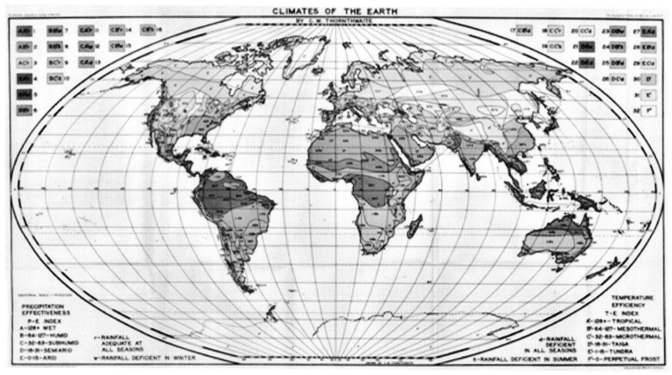

Figure 2. Climates of Earth (Thornthwaite 1931)

The Climate of South Texas: General Overview

The climate of this region has been variously described in the literature as marginal, vulnerable, anomalous and even as a "problem" climate (Le Houerou and Norwine 1987; Norwine 1978; Trewartha 1981; Norwine and Bingham 1985; Powley and Norwine 1992; Norwine et al. 1995; Norwine and Giardino 2002). It would not be inappropriate to add "puzzle, paradox or conundrum" to these descriptions. These characterizations are all apt because of the region's geography of in-betweenness. To begin with, it lies very near the intersection of two of Earth's three first-order climate divides, a very rare, and defining, circumstance. The first of these[2] is the somewhat ambiguous boundary between the "winterless" tropical regimes to the south and the seasonal, temperate or middle-latitude regimes to the north. Of course, this aspect of in-betweenness is why South Texas is characterized as "subtropical." The second is the division between the arid west and the moisture-surplus east, a north-south divide which extends right through South Texas. This feature of in-betweenness explains why this region is described as "semi-arid" (west) and "subhumid" (east) and why non-irrigated commercial, row-crop agriculture, which exists more or less continuously for a thousand miles eastward from the Atlantic Ocean, ends abruptly around Kingsville and for all practical purposes does not occur westward of South Texas all the way to the Pacific Ocean. Moreover, it is in-between the near-surface influence of the extremely moist prevailing southeasterly winds and the aridifying influence of the descending air associated with the Bermuda High to the east and the Pacific High to the west.

The result is a challenging, problematic regime. More specifically, South Texas has a regional climate which is dominated by three main aspects. It is:

- neotropical or megathermal, with high summer and annual temperatures [21.5-23.5°C, (about 70-75°F), i.e., not much lower than the Equator's approximately 26.5°C (80°F)], and mild winters with occasional severe or killing freezes (historically about one such per decade);

---

[2] excluding the subpolar divide, which separates the polar from the temperate lands

- both wet and dry: (a) near the surface the prevailing southeasterly winds bring copious quantities of moisture from the Gulf of Mexico, causing South Texas to experience higher atmospheric moisture contents (humidity levels) than any other part of the continental United States except southern Florida. However, due to the sinking action associated with the nearby subtropical Bermuda and Pacific Highs, (b) South Texas is climatically subhumid to semiarid, i.e., uniformly moisture-deficient because of limited annual rainfall of about 500-750 mm, (20-30 in), combined with high evapotranspiration rates (mean yearly potential evapotranspiration ranges from double to quadruple average annual precipitation); and,

- marginal or vulnerable (e.g., agriculturally and ecologically) in that most years are either significantly wetter or drier than the long-term average. In other words, rather than mean annual rainfall being "normal," it would be more accurate to describe it as "abnormal." Such unusually large interannual variabilities of precipitation, about 30% in eastern South Texas and about 40% in the west near Laredo, represent rainfall variability values more typically associated with many of the world's harshest semi-desert regions.

The result is a climate which is classified according to Thornthwaite's water-balance system (Thornthwaite 1948) as subtropical subhumid in the east and subtropical semiarid in the west but which older cowboys and farmers sometimes called "our desert jungle." In the entire northern hemisphere only the Persian Gulf area is comparably and counter-intuitively at once both wet <u>and</u> dry. It is indeed a fascinating regime but one which, from the standpoints of both natural and human ecologies and economies, should be thought of as having very little margin of error. In particular, any combination of future climate changes which would tend to exaggerate existing moisture deficiencies would be likely to have mainly negative implications for people and at least some biophysical/environmental aspects. Unfortunately, such a scenario appears increasingly likely given the evidence of the studies of climate change reported later in this chapter.

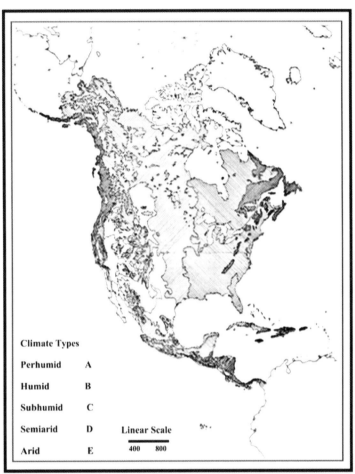

Figure 3. Moisture Regions of North America (Thornthwaite 1933 to 1948)

The Climate of South Texas: The Twentieth Century

Temperatures 1900 to 2000: Mean Annual. (Figure 4) The mean annual temperature for the period of 1900-2000 of a group of twenty-one stations[*] across South Texas was 22°C (71.5°F). For the sake of comparison and general interest, this average may be contrasted with such extremes as these:
- the 27°C (80.5°F) yearly thermal mean of Padang, Sumatra, located one degree South Latitude; and,
- the -3°C (26.7°F) annual temperature average for Fairbanks, Alaska.
- It is in fact because the mean annual temperature of South Texas is so near that of the Equator, and because winters are very mild with few killing freezes, that the region is described as "subtropical" (Figure 6).

19

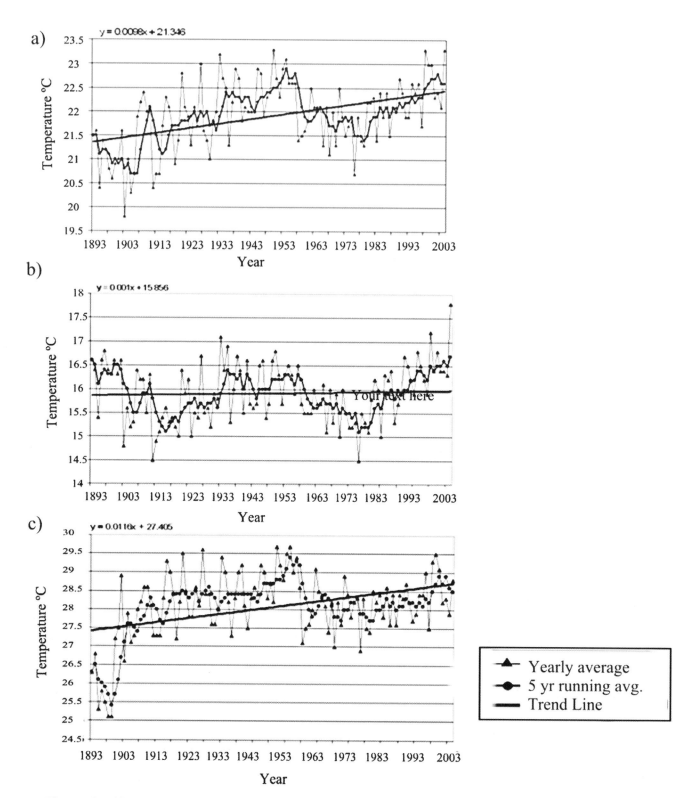

Figure 4. Mean annual temperature (a), mean annual minimum temperature (b), and mean annual maximum temperature (c) of South Texas during 1900 to 2000. Twenty-one Stations*: Eastern: Alice, Beeville, Corpus Christi, Falfurrias, Goliad, Kingsville, and Victoria; Western: Brackettville, Carrizo Springs, Dilley, Eagle Pass, Encinal, San Antonio, and Uvalde; Lower Valley: Brownsville, Harlingen, McAllen, Port Isabel, Raymondville, Rio Grande City, and Weslaco.

m

The average annual temperature for the period 1931 to 1965 (prior to 1931, many data are missing, hence the use of the 1931 to 1965 period) equaled 22.3°C (72.1°F), while that of 1966 to 2000, was 22.0°C (71.6°F), a very small decrease of 0.3°C (0.54°F) (Figure 6). Examination of a plot and table (Figure 4 and Table 2) of annual temperatures for the century reveals four interesting features:

- values generally trended upward through the first one-half of the twentieth century, then
- trended downward for about twenty-five years between approximately 1950 and 1975,
- on average declined slightly across the period of 1931 to 2001 (Figure 6), and
- have since about 1980 climbed markedly to 2000.

Several observations can be gathered from these findings. First, numerous studies have reported increasing planetary surface temperatures during the past century or so; i.e., "global warming" (Hansen et al. 2001; Rayner et al. 2003). Second, the Northern Hemisphere cooled slightly (0.5°C or 0.9°F) during the so-called Little Ice Age of about 1300-1900 CE. Many of the record cold temperatures in the South Texas region set during the 1890s were not shattered until brutally cold snaps on or around the Christmas days of 1983 and 1989. Third, various studies have reported that global mean temperatures decreased for about twenty-five years between the late 1940s and 1970 or so.

At the time this decrease was widely attributed to the so-called "human volcano," i.e., aerosols of anthropogenic origin, but most climate scientists now believe that it was in fact an expression of natural variability (Johannessen et al. 2004; Tourpali 2005). Fourth, it should be noted that the overall very slight decline of mean temperature in South Texas for much of the twentieth century is in line with observations from other sections of

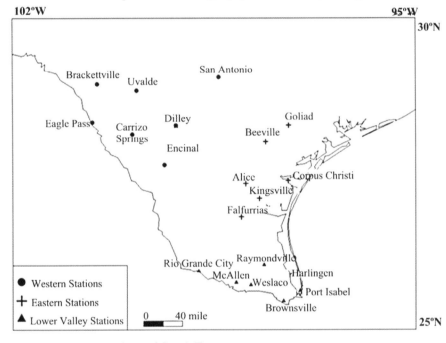

Figure 5. Three regions of South Texas

the southeastern United States, where mean temperatures did not reflect the global average increase during the period, possibly due to ocean-current effects. Finally, the sharp upturn seen in annual average temperatures during (especially) the last fifteen years of the century matches the often-reported worldwide thermal increase during that period (Zwiers and Zhang 2003; Karoly et al. 2003; Stott 2003).

Temperatures 1900 to 2000: Mean Minimum. (Figure 4b) The mean daily minimum temperature for the twenty-one station South Texas region during the twentieth century was 15.8°C (60.4°F). Broadly speaking, the pattern of average daily minimum temperature was similar to that described for the annual means: values trended upward till around mid-century, downward during the twenty-five years between about 1950 and the late 1970s, and then once again back upward to 2000. Comparing the period of 1931 to 1965 with that of 1966-2000, the mean daily minimum temperature for 1931 to 1965 was 16.1°C (61°F), while the average minimum for 1966-2000 was 15.9°C (60.6°F), a decrease of 0.2°C (0.4°F).

Temperatures 1900 to 2000: Mean Maximum. (Figure 4c) The twentieth century average daily maximum temperature for the region was 28.2°C (83.3°F). The mean maximum during 1931 to 1965 was 28.5°C (83.3°F), while the average for 1966 to 2000 was 28.2°C (82.8°F), a difference of -0.3°C (0.5°F). Once again, the temporal pattern was similar to that earlier described, with the notable exception that the upward trend near the end of the century began later, not being clearly evident until the late 1990s.

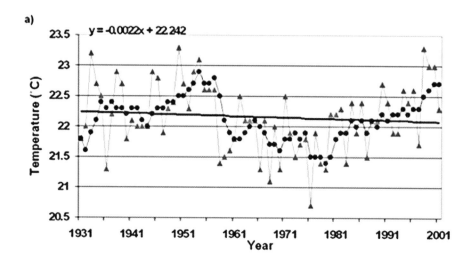

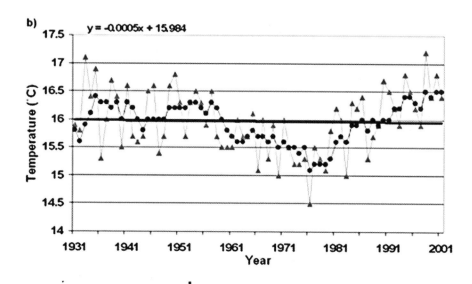

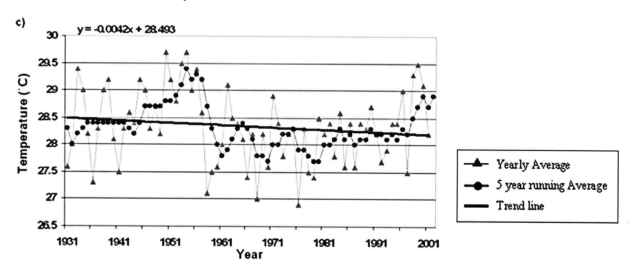

Figure 6. Mean annual temperature (a), mean annual minimum temperature (b), and mean annual maximum temperature (c) of South Texas* during 1931 to 2001. *Twenty-one Stations: Eastern: Alice, Beeville, Corpus Christi, Falfurrias, Goliad, Kingsville, and Victoria; Western: Brackettville, Carrizo Springs, Dilley, Eagle Pass, Encinal, San Antonio, and Uvalde; Lower Valley: Brownsville, Harlingen, McAllen, Port Isabel, Raymondville, Rio Grande City, and Weslaco.

Temperatures 1900 to 2000: Summary. South Texas mean temperatures decreased marginally from 1931 to 2000 (Figure 6), but also revealed a steady increase during the final twenty to twenty-five years of the century. (Note: post-2000 data reveal a continuation of this warming.)

Table 1. South Texas Regional Precipitation: 1900-2000

Period	Region	Mean Annual (mm)	Mean Summer (mm)	Mean Winter (mm)
Entire Twentieth Century: 1900 to 2000	South Texas Combined	660	411.5	247.1
	Eastern South Texas	761.6	462.7	299.3
	Western South Texas	592.6	377.5	214
	Southern South Texas	625.7	396.1	228.2
1931 to 1965 vs 1966 to 2000	South Texas Combined	622/710**	389/451**	233/262**
	Eastern South Texas	714/837**	429/529**	287/313**
	Western South Texas	572/623**	373/397	198/224**
	Southern South Texas	579/669**	366/429**	214/248**

**Difference significant at 0.01 confidence level

Precipitation 1900 to 2000: Mean Annual. (Figure 7a; Table 1) The mean annual precipitation, 1900 to 2000, for the entire twenty-one station South Texas region was 660 mm (26 in). The average for the period 1931 to 1965 was 622 mm (24 in), compared with an average of 710 mm (27.9 in) for 1966 to 2000, a difference of +88 mm (3.5 in), i.e., an increase of 13%.

As reported earlier, the year-to-year pattern is dominated by variability, with many "wet" years/periods and at least as many "dry" ones. For example, during this century, many of the hundred and one years were either "wet" years (P>90, N=30, where "P"=the 90th percentile) or "dry" years (P<10, N-31, where "P"=the 10th percentile). Particularly noteworthy among the latter was the infamous drought of 1950 to 1956, when the mean annual precipitation fell to 477.5 mm (18.8 in), with and only 350 mm (13.8 in) in 1956. This event caused widespread hardship throughout South Texas (Figure 8), and was a climatic phenomenon not experienced in the region since around the time of the Civil War (Figure 9). Also notable and following close on the heels of the 1950s drought, was that of 1961 to 1964 when the average yearly rainfall was only 500 mm (19.7 in). By contrast, during the twelve-year period of 1965 to 1976, the mean annual region-wide precipitation was 777 mm (30.6 in) and not a single year with significantly below-mean rainfall occurred. It would probably not be exaggerating to speculate that this prolonged relatively benign wet period lulled citizens and policy-makers into some degree of complacency vis-à-vis what constitutes "normal" rainfall in a semiarid region like South Texas.

Precipitation 1900 to 2000: Mean Summer Rainfall. (Figure 7b) The average annual summer (April to September) rainfall for the region was 411.5 mm (16.2 in). A majority of annual precipitation recorded across South Texas comes during this "high sun" period of April-September although this is perhaps by itself somewhat misleading. Because it is so hot, potential evapotranspiration or moisture loss in these months far exceeds the moisture "income" in the form of rains. In other words, somewhat counter-intuitively our rainy season is actually our driest or most moisture-deficient season.

A comparison of 1931 to 1965 with 1966 to 2000 reveals that mean summer rainfall increased 14%, from 389.2 mm (15.3 in) during 1931 to 1965 to 451.4 mm (17.8 in) in 1966 to 2000 but decreased very slightly over the entire period of 1931 to 2001 (Figure 8 and Table 1).

Examination of the century-long plot reveals that summer rainfall was even more prone to exaggerated variability than annual precipitation. This is not particularly surprising, as the six-month high-sun "summer" (April-September in the Northern Hemisphere) includes the rainfall-maximum month of September, during which the region frequently experiences heavy rains associated with hurricanes and lesser tropical disturbances. To note but one example of this variability, a "run" of relatively wet summers was experienced during the period of 1965 to 1981, when the average value was 524.3 mm (20.64 in). Summers of the following nineteen years were considerably drier: summer precipitation during 1982 to 2000 was only

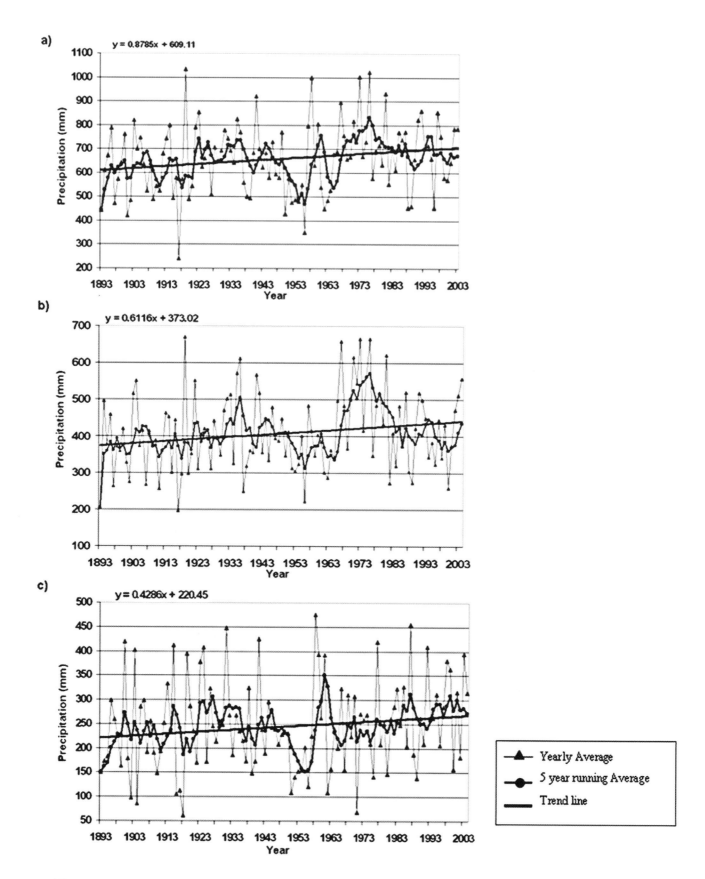

Figure 7. Mean annual total precipitation (a), mean annual summer* precipitation (b), and mean annual winter* precipitation (c) of South Texas during 1900 to 2000. *Summer includes precipitation from April to September and winter indicates October to March.

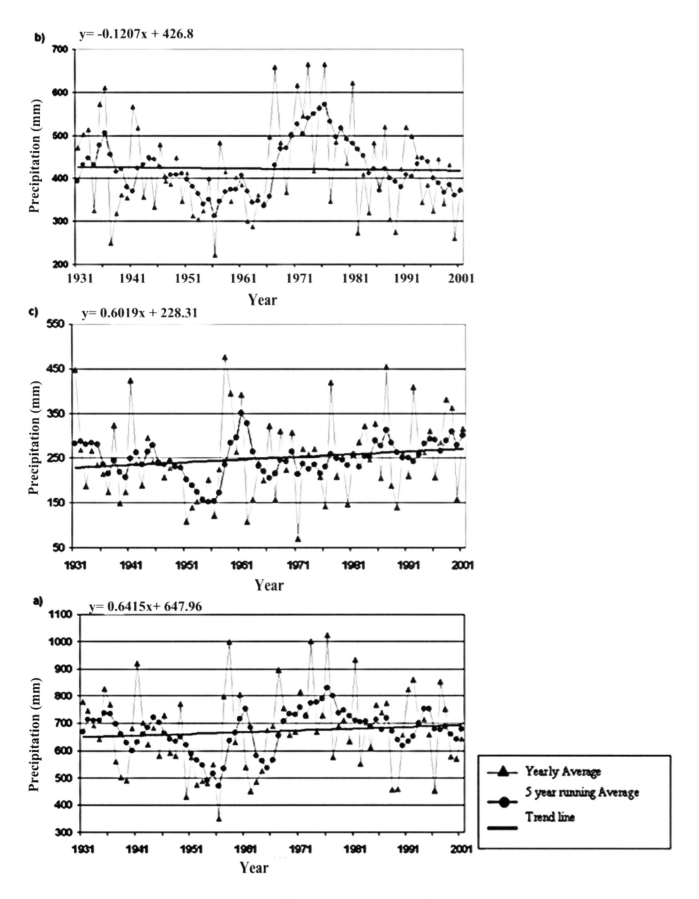

Figure 8. Mean annual total precipitation (a), mean annual summer* precipitation (b), and mean annual winter* precipitation (c) of South Texas during 1931 to 2001. *Summer includes precipitation from April to September and winter indicates October to March.

388.6 mm (15.3 in), a reduction of 26%. Importantly, the number of "wet" summers (P > 90, N = 23) was 38% smaller than the number of "dry" summers (P < 10, N = 37).

Precipitation 1900 to 2000: Mean Winter Precipitation. (Figure 7c.) Winters in South Texas are relatively dry. The average winter (October to March) precipitation for the century was 247.1 mm (9.73 in), only 37% of the yearly mean. However, as earlier noted, this figure can be deceiving. Because of the severe heat load and evaporation loss of South Texas' long, hot summers, our "dry" (i.e., limited rainfall) winters are actually the season when average monthly moisture deficiencies are smallest, i.e., when precipitation was closest to matching potential evapotranspiration.

The mean winter rainfall for 1931 to 1965 was 233.2 mm (9.2 in) compared with an average of 261.6 mm (10.3 in) for 1991 to 2000, an increase of 28.4 mm (1.12 in) or 11%, not much less than the 14% increase in summer rains and the overall annual 13% gain already observed. Typically, given the "normal" South Texas pronounced degree of inter-annual variability, the number of "dry" winters (P < 10, N = 30) exceeded the number of "wet" winters (P > 90, N = 28) by nearly 30%. Winter precipitation also increased on average during 1931 to 2001 (Figure 8c).

Precipitation 1900 to 2000: Summary. The most important pattern detected was a general *precipitation increase*. The regional average yearly precipitation for the entire century, 1900 to 2000, was at 660.4 mm (26 in) in line with previous studies (e.g., Norwine, Bingham and Zepeda 1978), but from 1931 to 1965 to 1966 to 2000 annual precipitation increased 13%, summer rains grew by 14%, and winter precipitation gained 11%. The singular exception was a decrease in mean summer rainfall over the 1931 to 2001 time frame. Secondarily, year-to-year precipitation region-wide means remained highly inconstant, as described in earlier reports (e.g., Norwine et al 1995). The "inconstancy" was that of pronounced inter-annual rainfall variability, with a majority of years falling into either the "wet" or "dry" categories.

The Climate of Three South Texas Regions:
The Twentieth-Century Regional Temperature Patterns and Trends.

Regional Mean Annual Daily Mean Temperature: 1900 to 2000. The mean annual temperature for the period 1900 to 2000 of eastern South Texas (Figure 10a) was 21.9°C (71.4°F). For western South Texas (Figure 10b), the average yearly temperature for the period was 21.2°C (70.2°F), and for southern South Texas (Figure 10c) the mean annual twentieth century temperature was 23.6°C (74.8°F).

Regional Mean Daily Maximum Temperature: 1900 to 2000. The mean maximum temperature for the period was 27.8°C (82°F) in the eastern region (Figure 11a), 28°C (82.4°F) in the west (Figure 11b), and 28.9°C (84°F) in the southern region (Figure 11c).

Regional Mean Daily Minimum Temperature: 1900 to 2000. The mean minimum temperature for the period was 16.1°C (61°F) in the east (Figure 12a), 14.5°C (58°F) in the west (Figure 12b), and 17.6 °C (63.7°F) in the south (Figure 12c).

Regional Temperature Trends, 1900 to 2000: Summary. In eastern, western, and southern South Texas, and also in the overall combined region, mean annual, mean maximum, and mean minimum temperatures were *very slightly lower*—i.e., cooled--comparing 1966 to 2000 with 1931 to 1965, and also across 1931 to 2001 (Figures 10 and 11, 11 and 12, and 12 and 13). Perhaps this finding should not be considered entirely surprising, as 1931 to 1965 included the exceptional dry/hot conditions associated with the infamous one hundred-year-event (see Figure 8 and 9) drought of 1950 to 1956. The finding is nonetheless noteworthy because it reveals that South Texas did not at least initially experience the worldwide increase of temperatures reported for the twentieth century (see Figure 22): i.e., no marked global warming "signal" was detected in this region through the majority of the last century. On the other hand, regional temperatures clearly did begin to trend markedly and nearly without annual exception upward during the final twenty years of the twentieth century, and were consequently higher at century's end than at its beginning (see Table 2, Figures. 11, 13, and 15).

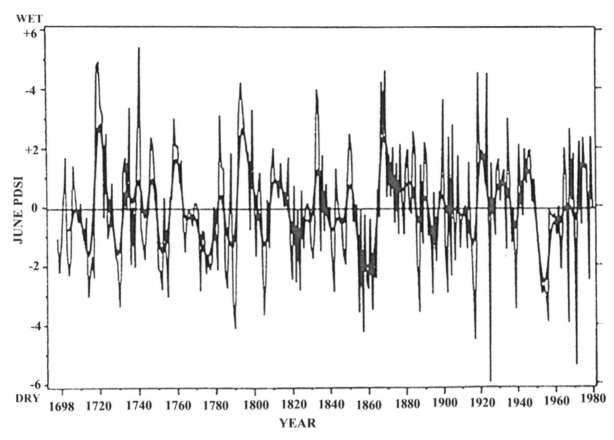

Figure 9. Reconstructed June Parmer Drought Sensitivity Index (PSDI) for South Texas plotted annually from 1698 to 1980, and smoothed with a low-pass filter passing variance with a frequency of greater than about eight years (Stahle and Cleaveland 1988)

Table 2. South Texas Regional Temperatures: 1900-2000

Period	Region	Mean Daily Mean (°C)	Mean Daily Maximum (°C)	Mean Daily Minimum (°C)
Entire Twentieth Century: 1900-2000	South Texas combined	22.0	28.2	15.8
	Eastern South Texas	21.9	27.8	16.1
	Western South Texas	21.2	28.0	14.5
	Southern South Texas	23.6	28.9	17.6
1931-1965 versus 1966-2000	South Texas combined	22.3/22.0	28.5/28.2	16.1/15.9
	Eastern South Texas	22.2/21.9	28.2/27.9	16.1/15.8
	Western South Texas	21.3/21.1	28.2/27.9	14.4/14.3
	Southern South Texas	23.3/23.1	29.0/28.7	17.7/17.5

Data from U.S. National Climatic Data Center; calculations by R. Bingham, Texas A&M University-Kingsville.

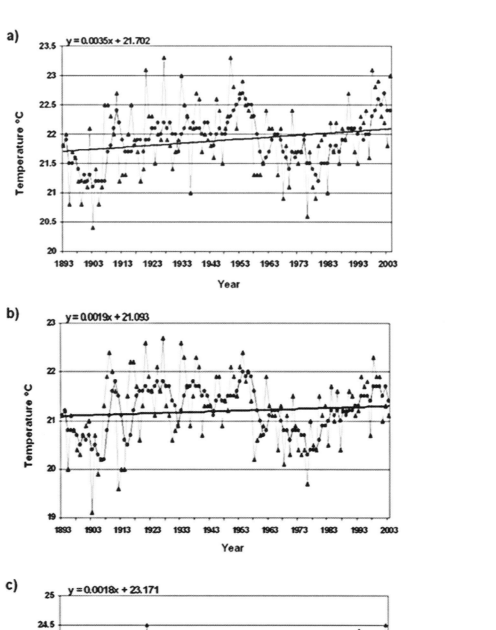

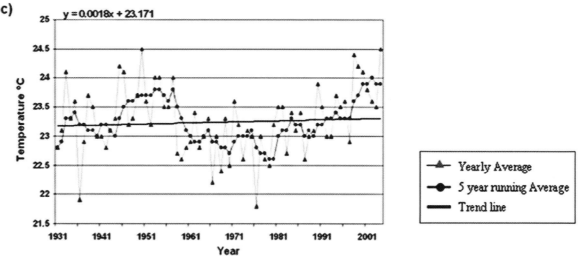

Figure 10. Mean annual temperature of eastern (a), western (b), and southern (c) stations during the twentieth century

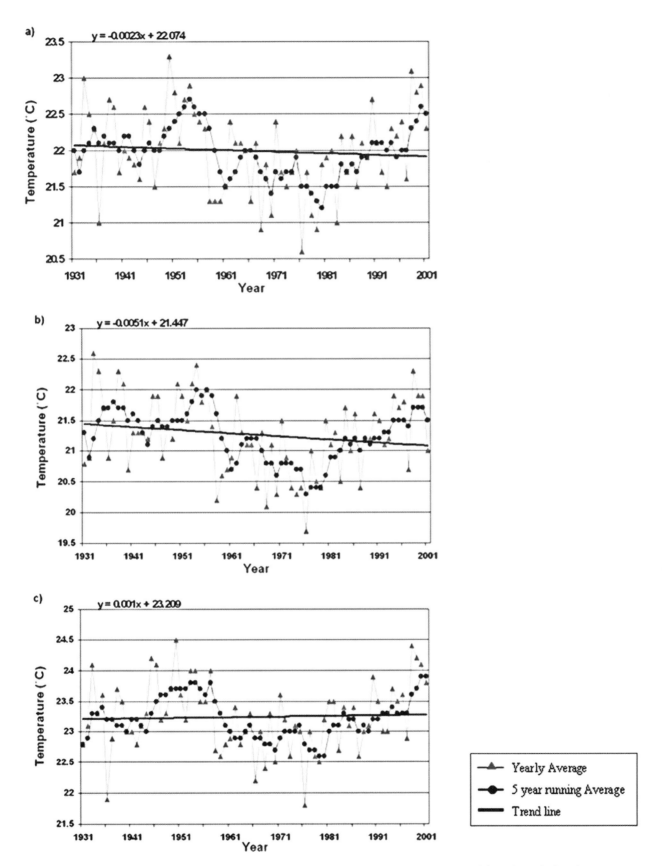

Figure 11. Mean annual temperature of eastern (a), western (b), and southern (c) stations during the 1931 to 2005 period

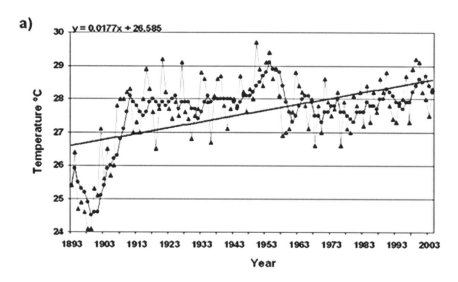

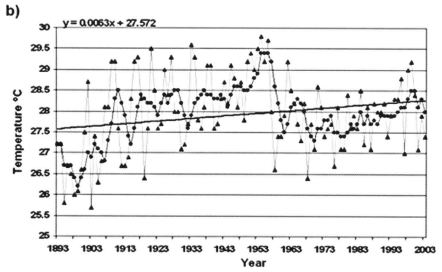

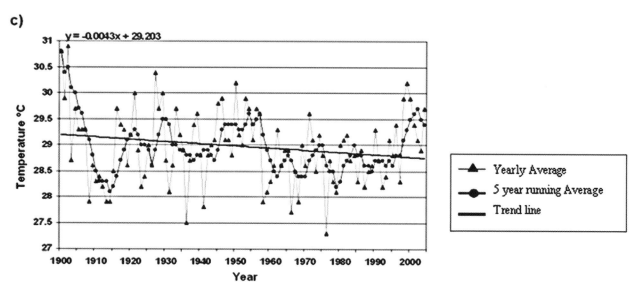

Figure 12. Mean annual maximum temperature of eastern (a), western (b), and southern (c) stations during the twentieth century

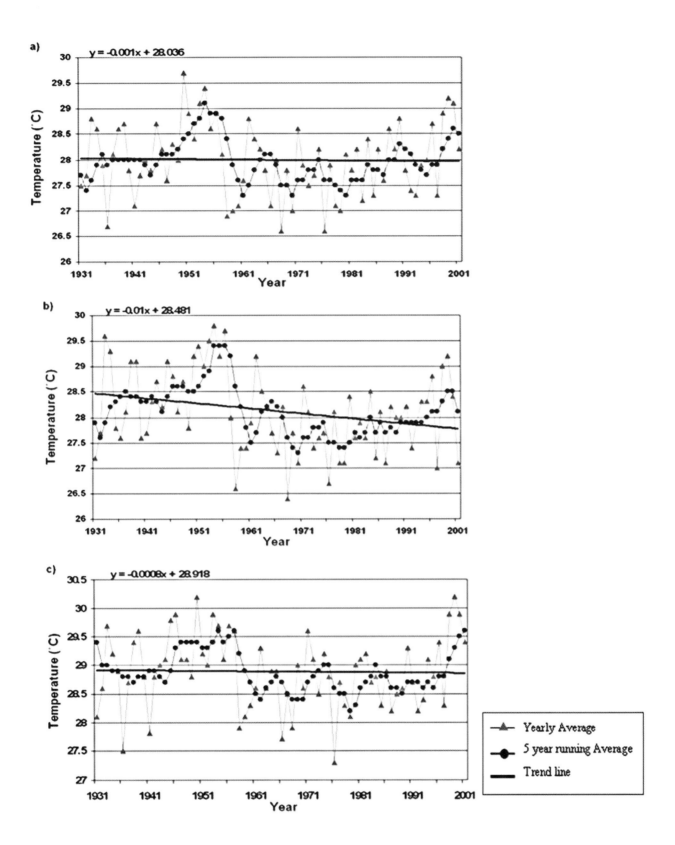

Figure 13. Mean annual maximum temperature of eastern (a), western (b), and southern stations during the1931 to 2001 period

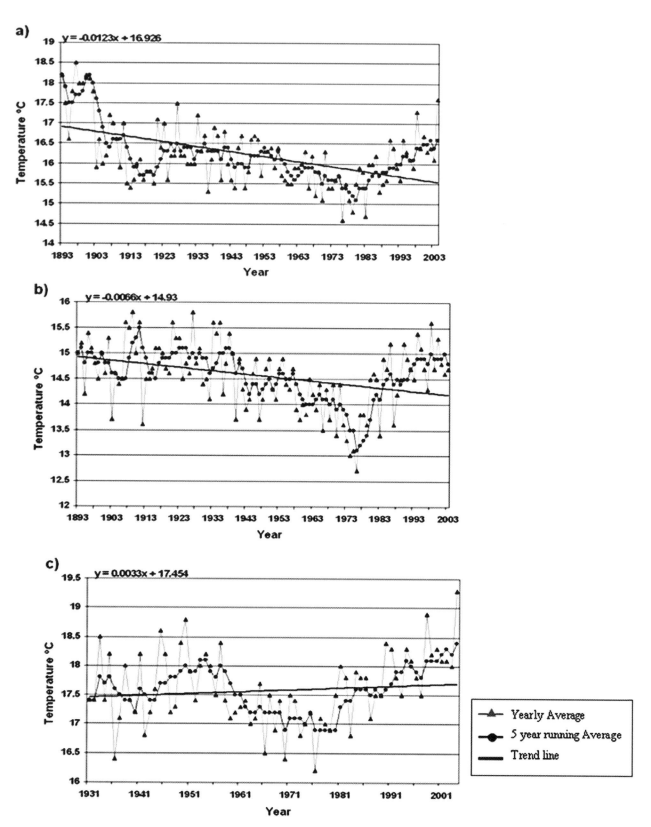

Figure 14. Mean annual minimum temperature of eastern (a), western (b), and southern
(c) stations during the twentieth century

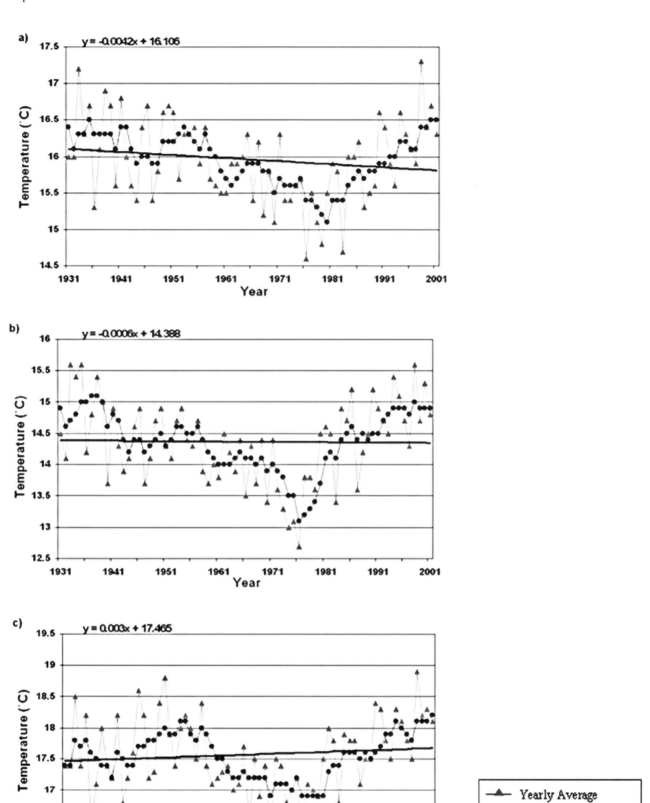

Figure 15. Mean annual minimum temperature of eastern (a), western (b), and southern (c) stations during 1931 to 2001 period

Regional Precipitation Patterns and Trends

Regional Mean Annual Precipitation: 1900 to 2000. The mean annual precipitation for the twentieth century, 1900 to 2000, was 761.6 mm (30 in) in eastern South Texas (Figure 16a), 592.6 mm (23.3 in) in western South Texas (Figure 16b), and 625.7 mm (24.6 in) in southern South Texas (Figure 16c).

Regional Mean Summer Precipitation: 1900 to 2000. As earlier noted, the mean annual summer (April to September) twentieth-century precipitation across the entirety of South Texas, 389 mm (15.3 in) during 1931-1965, increased by 14% to 451 mm (17.8 in) during 1966-2000. Regionally, average yearly summer rainfall (1900-2000) was 462.7 mm (18.2 in) in the east (Figure 18a), 377.5 mm (14.9 in) in the west (Figure 18b), and 396.1 mm (15.6 in) in the south (Figure 18c).

Comparing 1931 to 1965 with 1966 to 2000, mean summer rainfall increased 19% from 429 mm (16.9 in) to 529 mm (20.8 in) in the east, 6% from 373 (14.7 in) to 397 mm (15.6 in) in the west, and 15% from 366 (14.4 in) to 429 mm (16.9 in) in the south. Figure 19 reveals that during 1931 to 2001 mean summer precipitation increased only in eastern South Texas but decreased slightly in the southern and western regions.

Regional Mean Winter Precipitation: 1900 to 2000. The mean annual winter (October to March) precipitation for the entire century was 299.3 mm (11.8 in) in eastern South Texas (Figure 20a), 214 mm (8.4 in) in western South Texas (Figure 20b), and 228.2 m (9.0 in) in southern South Texas (Figure 20c). Comparing 1931 to 1965 with 1966 to 2000, mean winter precipitation increased 8% from 287 mm (11.3 in) to 313 mm (12.3in) in the east, 12% from 198 mm (7.8 in) to 224 mm (8.8 in) in the west, and 14% from 214 mm (8.4 in) to 248 mm (9.8 in) in the south. Interestingly, for the entirely of 1931 to 2001, mean winter precipitation increased in all three subregions (Figure 21).

Regional Precipitation Trends, 1900 to 2000: Eastern South Texas. Precipitation in the twentieth century in eastern South Texas (Figure 16) reveals a pattern very similar to that earlier observed for the entirety of South Texas but one wetter across the board. The average yearly precipitation, 1900 to 2000, for eastern South Texas was 761.6 mm (30 in) compared to 660 mm (26 in) for all of South Texas. Mean summer rainfall was 462.7 mm (18 in) in the east, 411.5 (16.2 in) across the total region. Mean eastern winter precipitation was 299.3 mm (11.8 in), and 247.1 mm (9.7 in) in South Texas as a whole. Obviously and unsurprisingly given its proximity to the Gulf of Mexico, eastern South Texas has been the most moisture-rich part of subtropical southern Texas.

The single most important trend detected was one of increasing precipitation. As previously described, eastern precipitation increased annually (15%) and in both summer (19%) and winter (8%) when the periods 1931 to 1965 and 1966 to 2000 are compared, and also increased on average during 1931 to 2001 (Figure 21).

Average yearly precipitation may also be somewhat more subjectively characterized as having trended upward following the droughts of 1950 to 1956 and 1961 to 1963, such that the approximately twenty years following 1964 were the wettest two decades of the period. The remaining years of the century seemed typically characterized by (a) inter-annual variability, (b) the first three-year drought since the early 1960s, that of 1988 to 1989, and finally, (c) a continuation of an upward trend of mean rainfall.

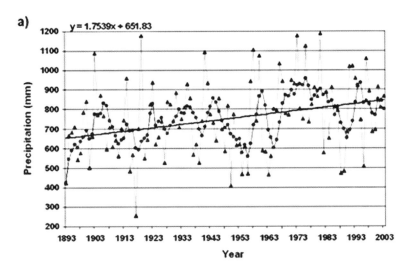

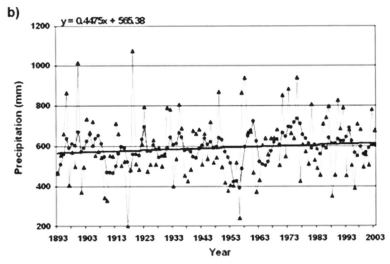

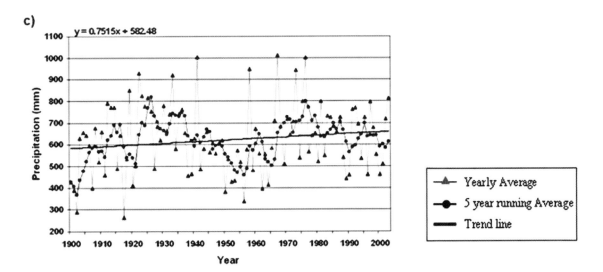

Figure 16. Mean annual total precipitation of eastern (a), western (b), and southern (c) stations during 1900 to 2000

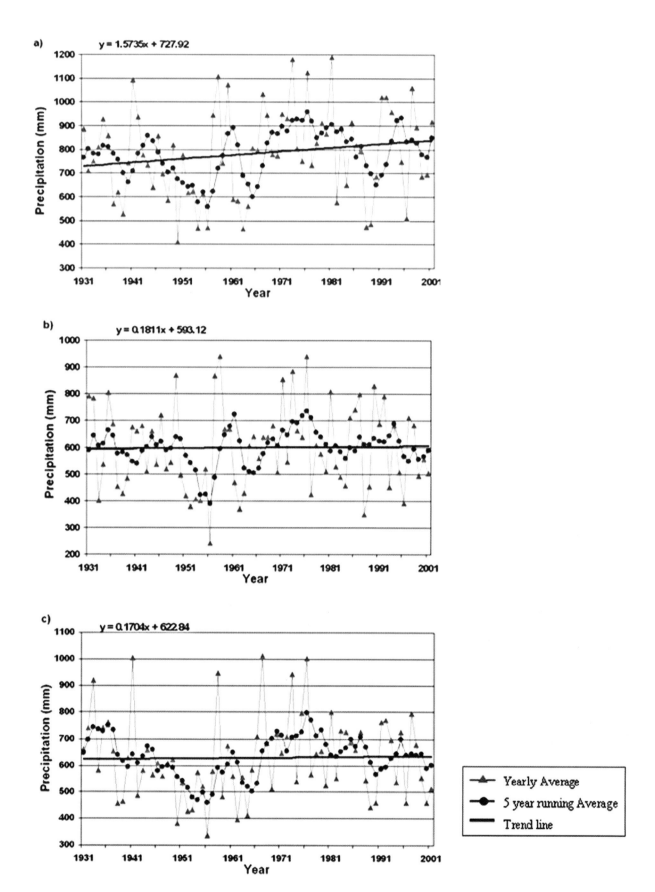

Figure 17. Mean annual total precipitation of eastern (a), western (b), and southern (c) stations during 1931 to 2001

Regional Precipitation Trends, 1900 to 2000: **Western South Texas**. Because western South Texas is located nearly as close to the aridifying influences of the Chihuahuan Desert to the west as it is to those of the Gulf of Mexico to the east, it is normally much drier than eastern South Texas. In fact, in Thornthwaite's moisture-balance climatic classification, the west is a completely different climatic type (semiarid) compared to that of the east (dry subhumid) (Figure 3). The statistics for the twentieth century verify this distinction. The average yearly precipitation, 1900 to 2000, for western South Texas was 592.6 mm (23 in) compared to 660 mm (26 in) for all of South Texas. Mean summer rainfall was 377.5 mm (14.9 in) in the west, 411.5 (16.2 in) across the total region. Mean western winter precipitation was 214 mm (8.4 in), 247.1 mm (9.7 in) in South Texas as a whole.

The trend of increasing precipitation from the period 1931 to 1965 to 1966 to 2000 was also true in the west: western precipitation increased annually (8%) and in both summer (6%) and winter (12%). On the other hand, Figures 17, 19, and 21 reveal that across the entirety of 1931 to 2001 mean annual precipitation was approximately "flat" due to a rough balance between increased winter and decreased summer rains.

Two other winter-precipitation patterns may be noted in passing:
- interannual variability was typically pronounced: of the hundred-and-one years in the period 1900 to 2000, a majority were either "wet" or "dry"; and,
- the plot (Figure 19b) of western-region winter precipitation, which comprises only about 36% of the yearly average, reveals the severity of the downturn during the drought of 1950 to 1956.

Regional Precipitation Trends, 1900 to 2000: Southern South Texas. The southern region of Texas is wetter than the west, and drier than the east. The average yearly precipitation, 1900 to 2000, for southern South Texas was 625.7 mm (24.6 in) compared to 660 mm (26 in) for all of South Texas. Mean summer rainfall was 396.1 mm (15.6 in) in the south, 411.5 mm (16.2 in) across the total region. Mean southern winter precipitation was 228.2 mm (9 in), 247.1 mm (9.7 in) in South Texas as a whole. The trend of increasing precipitation from the period 1931 to 1965 to 1966 to 2000 found in the east and west was also true in the south: southern precipitation increased annually (14%) and in both summer (15%) and winter (14%). However, as in the west, during the entire period of 1931 to 2001, mean southern summer rainfall decreased while winter precipitation increased on average with the result that mean annual totals remained about constant (Figs. 17, 19, and 21).

Otherwise, examination of the precipitation graphs (Figures 16 to 21) for southern South Texas reveals a pattern similar to that noted for the east: mean annual and especially mean summer values experienced a prolonged period of roughly two decades of decline centered on the infamous drought of 1950 to 1956. This was followed by an approximately equal period of mostly above-average rainfall, which was in turn followed by a return to a pattern of extreme year-to-year variability and, for summer precipitation, decline (Figure 19). By contrast, mean winter rainfall increased during the final decades of the century (Figure 21).

Regional Precipitation Trends, 1900 to 2000: Summary. Eastern South Texas was consistently the wettest part of South Texas, and the western region was the driest. All the regions experienced increased precipitation annually and in both summer and in winter during 1966 to 2000 than they did during 1931 to 1965. Across the span of 1931 to 2001 (Figs. 17, 19, and 21), eastern-region mean precipitation increased in winter, summer, and annually, while in the west and south average summer rains decreased while winter rainfall increased.

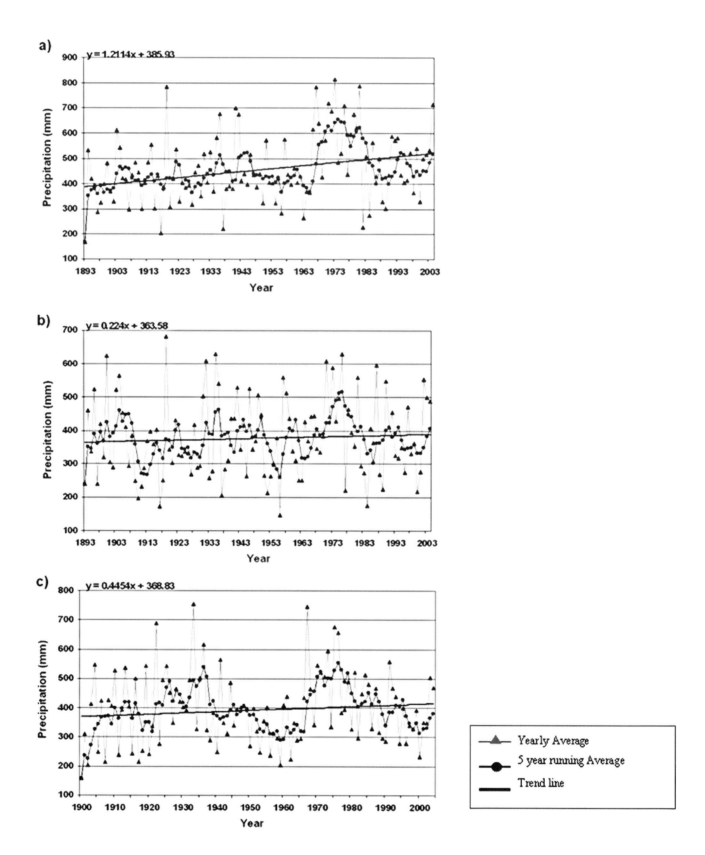

Figure 18. Mean annual summer total precipitation of eastern (a), western (b), and southern (c) stations during the twentieth century

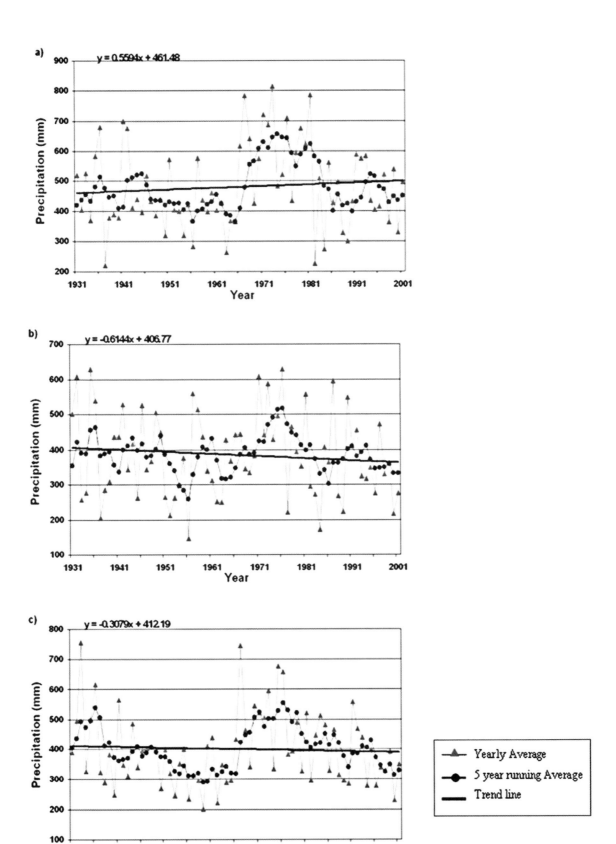

Figure 19. Mean annual summer total precipitation of eastern (a), western (b), and southern (c) stations during the 1931 to 2001 period

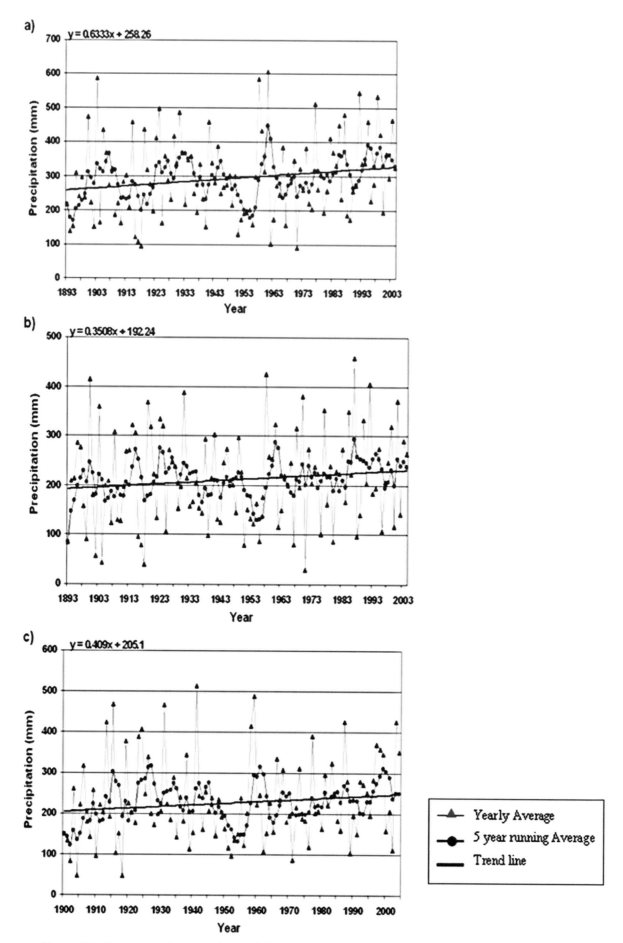

Figure 20. Mean annual winter total precipitation of eastern (a), western (b), and southern (c) stations during the twentieth century

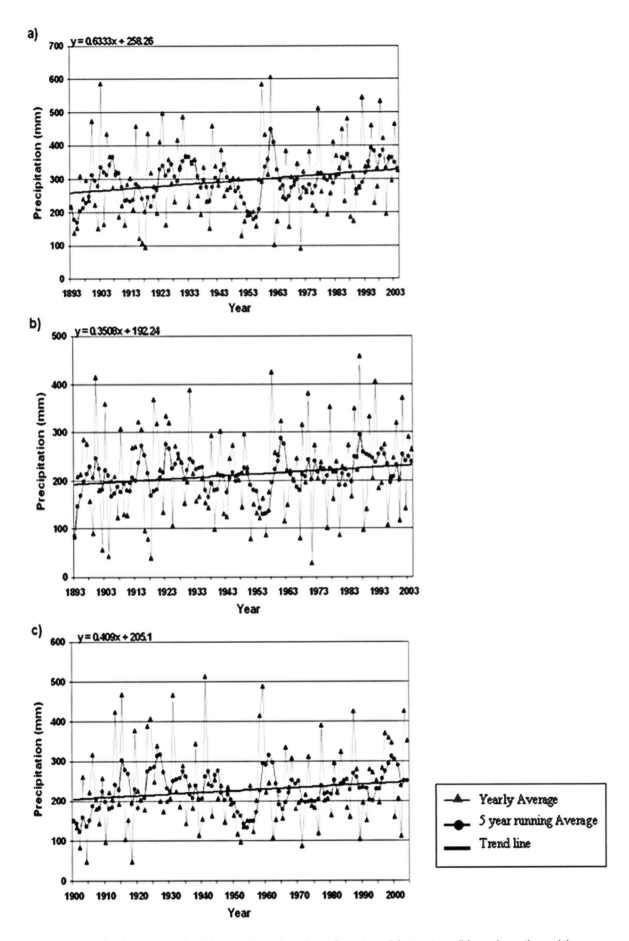

Figure 21. Mean annual winter total precipitation of eastern (a), western (b), and southern (c) stations during the 1931-2001 period

To recapitulate:

- Mean annual precipitation during 1931 to 1965 was 714 mm (28.1 in) in the east, 572 mm (22.5 in) in the west, and 579 mm (22.8 in) in the south. Mean summer rainfall for that period was 429 mm (16.9 in) in the east, 373 mm (14.7 in) in the west, and 336 mm (13.2 in) in the south. Mean winter precipitation was 287 mm (11.3 in) in the east, 198 mm (7.8 in) in the west, and 214 mm (8.4 in) in the south.

- During 1966 to 2000, mean annual precipitation was 837 mm (32.9 in) in the east, 623 mm in the west, and 669 mm (26.3 in) in the south. Mean summer rainfall for that period was 529 mm (20.8 in) in the east, 397 mm (15.6 in) in the west, and 429 mm (16.8 in) in the south. Mean winter precipitation was 313 mm (12.3in) in the east, 224 mm in the west, and 248 in the south.

On one hand, the importance or significance of this suggestion of increasing precipitation should not be exaggerated and certainly not taken to necessarily represent, for example, evidence of a global warming effect. Firstly, as has been seen the normal climate of South Texas and its internal regions is one of wide swings from wet to dry. In the semiarid subtropics, especially those locations in the hurricane belt, many years and some decades are wetter, and even more are drier, than the long-term average. Secondly, although planet Earth warmed during the twentieth century and even South Texas exhibited some warming late in the century, and although increased planetary surface/ocean temperatures are expected to lead to increased mean annul precipitation, not every place or region on Earth will become wetter as the world warms, and even where such is the case an expected increase in extreme-events (downpours and dry spells) will tend in the future to inhibit actual on-the-ground precipitation effectiveness.

On the other hand, it is hardly an exaggeration to note that an increase in precipitation over several generations in a semiarid region like South Texas is good news. In fact, this pattern might arguably be considered the most sanguine single finding of this brief sketch of the region's twentieth century climate.

Global Warming and the Future Climate of South Texas: The Twenty-first Century

Earth is getting warmer. There is no longer any real dispute about that. *Why* it is warming is a bit more contentious but most climate scientists today would answer, "because of humans." This owes especially to greenhouse gas emissions presently mainly the USA and other developed countries, although projections suggest that rapidly developing countries such as India and China will be among the leaders by mid-century. With respect to the key "So what?" question, the answers to the most difficult climate change questions — the rate of warming and its eventual consequences for and impacts on people — remain somewhat more up for grabs so to speak but even here we believe that answers are becoming ever clearer and more disturbing. Just to mention a single example, a recent study by M. Scholze of Bristol University (U.K.) indicates a "tipping point" toward the middle of this century with such potentially devastating impacts as the loss of half the world's forests (Jha 2006) owing to a mean worldwide temperature increase of about 3°C.

Through the use of climate modeling and expert-team "scenario" analyses, scientists can offer answers about the future climate of South Texas which are accurate within reasonable error-ranges in order to help provide some guidance to citizens, educators, and policy leaders. The following brief background overview of the state of knowledge about global warming is based on the findings from two assessments, one carried out internationally and one carried out nationally. We refer to the 2001 report of the Intergovernmental Panel on Climate Change (IPCC) and the National Academy of Sciences (NAS) June 6, 2001, report, "Climate Change Science: Analysis of Some Key Questions."

The IPCC assessments took years to prepare and represents the work of hundreds of scientific authors worldwide. It is based on the scientific literature, and was carefully scrutinized by hundreds of scientific peers through an extensive peer review process. The independent NAS report was a consensus report compiled by an eleven-member panel of leading U.S. climate scientists, including a mix of scientists who have been skeptical about some findings of the IPCC and other assessments on climate change.

First, two fundamental issues of importance must be emphasized. These have been long-known, are very well understood, and have been deeply underscored in all previous reports and other such scientific summaries.[3]

---

[3] Please note that key findings of the most recent IPCC reports [2007] are summarized in Chapter One by Gerald North, this volume.

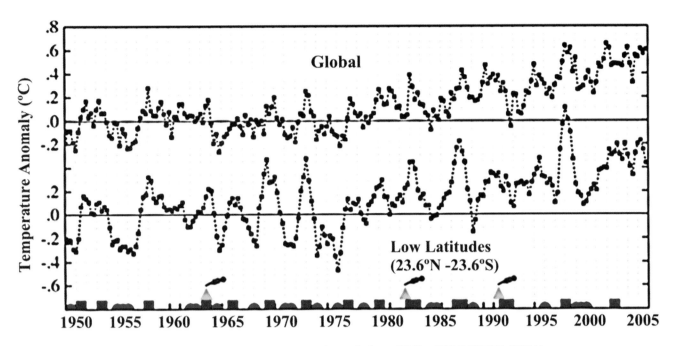

Figure 22. Temperature index change at seasonal resolution: 1950 - 2005 (IPCC, 2001)

The Natural Greenhouse Effect. The natural greenhouse effect has existed for many millions of years and has been very beneficial to humans. Because most of the gases in Earth's atmosphere are transparent to the very penetrating, short-wave energy emitted by the sun, most of the solar radiation which reaches the atmosphere passes through it and is absorbed by the earth. A portion of 35% or so is reflected back to space, mainly by clouds, the so-called planetary albedo. Because Earth is far cooler than the sun, it mostly gives off longer wave-length heat energy. About 2% of the atmosphere consists of the so-called "greenhouse" gases, notably carbon dioxide and water vapor, which absorb the outgoing terrestrial energy quite efficiently. This temporary "trapping" is referred to as the greenhouse effect. Because the excess heat escapes to space at night, Earth remains in approximate heat balance, that is, starts each day off with a "clean slate" with respect to this process. However, the greenhouse effect has increased Earth's surface temperature very slowly and incrementally by about 15.5°C (60°F) according to an estimation by many scientists. Considering that the planetary mean surface temperature is coincidentally almost precisely 14.4°C (58°F) at present, all humans should be grateful for the natural greenhouse effect.

The "Unnatural" Greenhouse Effect. However, too much of even a good thing can be bad, and that is the case with respect to our ongoing augmentation or stimulation of the greenhouse effect. Burning coal, oil and natural gas to heat our homes, power our cars, and illuminate our cities produces carbon dioxide and other greenhouse gases as by-products. Deforestation and clearing of land for agriculture also release significant quantities of such gases. Over the last century, we have been emitting greenhouse gases to the atmosphere faster than natural processes can remove them. During this time, atmospheric levels of these gases have climbed steadily and are projected to continue their steep ascent as global economies grow.

Direct atmospheric measurements made over the past forty-plus years have documented the steady growth in the atmospheric abundance of carbon dioxide. In addition to these direct real-time measurements, ice cores have revealed the atmospheric carbon dioxide concentrations of the distant past. Measurements using air bubbles trapped within layers of accumulating snow show that atmospheric carbon dioxide has increased by more than 30% over the Industrial Era (since 1750), compared to the relatively constant abundance that it had over the preceding seven hundred and fifty years of the past millennium. The predominant cause of this increase in carbon dioxide is the combustion of fossil fuels and the burning of forests. Further, methane abundance has doubled over the Industrial Era, but its increase has slowed over the recent decade for reasons not clearly understood. Other heat-trapping gases are also increasing as a result of human activities. Scientists are unable to state with certainty the exact rate at which these gases will continue to increase because of uncertainties in future emissions as well as how these emissions will be taken up by the atmosphere, land, and oceans. However, it is certain that once in the atmosphere, these greenhouse gases have a relatively long life-time, in the order of decades to centuries. This means that most of these gases become well mixed throughout the globe (IPCC 2001; Nakicenovic and Swart 2000; Hansen et al., 2005a,b). So what? The increase in greenhouse gas concentrations in the atmosphere implies a positive radiative forcing, i.e., a tendency to warm the climate system.

There is a growing set of observations that yields a collective picture of a warming world over the past century. The global-average surface temperature has increased over the twentieth century by 0.4 to 0.8°C (0.7 to 1.4°F). This occurred both over land and the oceans. The average temperature increase in the Northern Hemisphere over the twentieth century is likely to have been the largest of any century during the past thousand years based on "proxy" data (and their uncertainties) from tree rings, corals, ice cores, and historical records. The 1990s are likely to have been the warmest decade and 1998 the warmest year of the past thousand years. Other observed changes are consistent with this warming. There has been a widespread retreat of mountain glaciers in non-polar regions. Snow cover, sea ice extent, sea ice thickness, and the duration of ice on lakes and rivers have all decreased. Ocean heat content has increased significantly since the late 1940s, the earliest time when we have adequate computer compatible records. The global-average sea level has risen between 10 to 20 centimeters (4 to 8 in), which is consistent with a warmer ocean occupying more space because of the thermal expansion of sea water and loss of land ice. There is an extensive literature on the broad trends and related impacts of recent global warming (e.g., Karl et al. 2006; IPCC 2001; NAST 2000).[4]

It is likely that the frequency of heavy and extreme precipitation events has increased as global temperatures have risen. This is particularly evident in areas where precipitation has increased, primarily in the mid and high latitudes of the Northern Hemisphere. Other extremes have decreased such as the frequency of extremely cold weather and the frequency of frost during the period of the instrumental record , e.g., fifty to two hundred years depending on location. Recent detailed studies of the impacts of changing patterns of regional climate extremes has been reported by Meehl and Tebaldi 2004; Meehl et al. 2004; and Meehl et al. 2005).

There is new and stronger evidence that most of the warming observed over the last fifty years is attributable to human activities. The 1995 IPCC climate-science assessment report concluded: "The balance of evidence suggests a discernible human influence on global climate." There is now a longer and more closely scrutinized observed temperature record. Climate models have evolved and improved significantly since the previous assessment. Although many of the sources of uncertainty identified in 1995 still remain to some degree, new evidence, longer and more precise data sets, and improved understanding support the updated conclusion. Namely, recent analyses have compared the surface temperatures measured over the last thousand, one hundred and forty, and fifty years to those simulated by mathematical models of the climate system, thereby evaluating the degree to which human influences can be detected. Both natural climate-change agents (solar variation and episodic, explosive volcanic eruptions) and human-related agents (greenhouse gases and aerosols) were included. The natural climate-change agents alone do not explain the warming (Meehl et al., 2004c; Hansen et al., 2005).

Scenarios of future human activities indicate continued changes in atmospheric composition throughout the twenty-first century. The atmospheric abundances of greenhouse gases and aerosols over the next hundred years cannot be predicted with high confidence, since the future emissions of these species will depend on many diverse factors, e.g., world population, economies, technologies, and human choices, which are not uniquely specifiable. Rather, the IPCC assessment aimed at establishing a set of scenarios of greenhouse gas and aerosol abundances, with each based on a picture of what the world plausibly could be over the twenty-first century. Based on these scenarios and the estimated uncertainties in climate models, the resulting projection for the global average temperature increases by the year 2100 ranges from 1.3 to 5.6°C (2.3 to 10.1°F). Approximately half of the uncertainty in this range is due to model uncertainties related to feedback effects and half is due to different scenarios of future emissions. Regardless of these uncertainties, such a projected rate of warming would be much larger than the observed twentieth century changes and would very likely be without precedent during at least the last ten thousand years. The corresponding projected increase in global sea level by the end of this century ranges from 9 to 88 cm (4 to 35 in). Uncertainties in the understanding of some climate processes make it more difficult to project meaningfully the corresponding changes in regional climate. Of course, future climate change will depend on the technological developments that enable reductions of greenhouse gas emissions. There is a basic scientific aspect that has been underscored

---

[4] The U. S. Global Change Research Program provides excellent background resources on climate variability and change [http://www.usgcrp.gov].

with very high confidence in all of the IPCC climate-science assessment reports (1990, 1995, and 2001). It is repeated here because it is a key (perhaps "the" key) aspect of a greenhouse-gas-induced climate change:

A greenhouse-gas warming could be reversed only very slowly. This quasi-irreversibility arises because of the slow rate of removal (over centuries) from the atmosphere of many of the greenhouse gases and because of the slow response of the oceans to thermal changes. For example, several centuries after carbon dioxide emissions occur about a quarter of the increase in the atmospheric concentrations caused by these emissions is projected to still be in the atmosphere. Additionally, global average temperature increases and rising sea levels are projected to continue for hundreds of years after a stabilization of greenhouse gas concentrations (including a stabilization at today's abundances), owing to the long time scales (decades to centuries) on which the deep ocean adjusts to climate change. Because of its large specific heat capacity and mass, the world ocean can store large amounts of heat and remove this heat from direct contact with the atmosphere for long periods of time.

The analysis of climate model results using elegant statistical methods is rapidly advancing knowledge of the most damaging impacts of climate change (e.g., Tebaldi et al. forthcoming). It is clear that natural hazards like urban heat waves, extreme precipitation, and changes in frost days will have potentially important regional impacts on both humans and nature (Meehl and Tebaldi 2004; Meehl et al. 2004a; Meehl et al. 2004b; Meehl et al. 2005; Hansen 2005). It is urgent that the implications of these scientific findings be considered in the context of South Texas futures.

Causes for Concern: Potential Consequences of Global Warming for South Texas

Some of the more important potential specific climate-changes which are likely to be spun off by global warming and which may present particular challenges, even threats, to southern Texas in the twenty-first century are as follows: more high-intensity rainfall events; increases in the average summer heat index and the frequency of "hot days" ; net soil moisture declines; increased number of "hot nights" (i.e., temperature minima greater than 26.7°C (80.06°F)); reduced frequency of sub-freezing temperatures, especially significant freezes, perhaps so much so that South Texas becomes in effect "tropical"; increased evapotranspiration rates due to higher temperatures coupled with unchanged precipitation rates resulting in much drier annual net moisture balances, i.e., greater deficiencies; and, consequent shifting of easternmost South Texas from subhumid to semiarid and westernmost South Texas from semiarid to semi- or near-desert regimes.

Possible Regional III Effects: In turn, a variety of possible impacts or consequences of these climate changes have been identified. A short list of the most important categories of effects might appear something like the following:

- **Water:** The vulnerability of both water supply and water quality to drought remains a serious issue that could be significantly enhanced by climate warming. However, our climate models are not yet entirely reliable with respect to predicting whether, much less exactly how much, wetter or dryer South Texas will be in 2100 and beyond.
- **Sea-level rise:** Sea-level rise, coupled with storm surges associated with tropical storms, could produce a myriad of severe negative economic and ecological consequences for coastal areas.
- **Agriculture**: Increased evapotranspiration rates, drier moisture balances, and an increased frequency of extreme weather events (e.g., high-intensity rainfall) could potentially threaten the viability of commercial agriculture in South Texas.
- **Health effects**: Potential negative health consequences range from the possible spread of infectious diseases such as dengue fever and malaria into South Texas to exacerbated respiratory and circulatory problems related to higher temperatures and reduced air quality, especially in urban areas.
- **Air quality:** Most large metropolitan areas in Texas currently face an air pollution crisis. High temperatures enhance the formation of ground-level ozone and other toxic chemicals associated with smog. Global warming will increase the length of the already long smog season in Texas. Increasing temperatures will also increase the demand for air conditioning, which will increase the use of electricity, with consequence increases in emissions of smog-forming gases from fossil fuel power plants.
- **Ecological/environmental consequences:** Flora and fauna had time to adapt to the relatively slow rate of most natural climate change, e.g., the 12.8°C (9°F) warming during the Holocene, the ten thousand years since the last Ice Age. The rate of global warming and associated other climate changes which are anticipated for the next century is many times more rapid, so much so that all that can be said at this early stage is that impacts on ecological systems are almost bound to be very significant.

- **Demographic and economic effects:** South Texas is a relatively poor region of rapidly increasing population, most of which is concentrated in a handful of urban centers and corridors such as San Antonio, Corpus Christi, Laredo, and the Lower Rio Grande Valley. The existing limits of physical geography[5] are almost certain to be exacerbated by greenhouse warming in ways which will have potentially serious demographic and economic implications. For example, if the annual moisture balance of the region is 25% drier later this century, how many people can it support? What happens to the regional economy if warming and drying means that commercial agriculture becomes non-sustainable? Could Corpus Christi or Brownsville be devastated sometime in mid-twenty-first century by a combination of a major hurricane and sea-level rise? Hint: think Hurricane "Katrina" to get some idea of the possibilities.

- **Indirect impacts of climate change at larger-than-regional scales:** Some major impacts of climate variability and change in South Texas could result from changes at larger scales, e.g., the 1998 Mexican fires; the increased illegal immigration after Hurricane Mitch in Central America; or the relation of immigration from tropical latitudes and the possible future expansion of the zone of occurrence of infectious diseases such as malaria.

- **Surprises and uncertainties**: Some of climate change will be unanticipated leading to significant surprises and uncertainties.

- **Options for adaptation to climate change:** There are almost certainly various actions and options which might make adaptation to and mitigation of climate change so that, for example, agriculture remains viable in the region. That such adaptations need to be explored seems particularly clear considering that some of the trends listed above, such as population and economic growth are likely to lead to severe water imbalances, i.e., greater deficiencies, even before climate change becomes a significant contributing factor (Powley and Norwine 1992).

Simulating the Climate of the Twenty-First Century

How might this regional climate change during the current century? A statistical model (Tebaldi et al. 2004, 2005) synthesizes the information contained in an ensemble of twenty-one state-of-the-art Global Climate Models (GCMs), run under historical conditions and the same, relatively conservative, future scenario of greenhouse gas emissions. The results are Probability Distribution Functions (PDFs) of monthly temperature and precipitation change for three future periods, as regional averages, the region encompassing southern Texas and Northern Mexico.

The statistical assumptions are formulated so that two criteria of model reliability are going to determine the way the twenty-one members of the ensemble are "weighted in," i.e. contribute to shape, the PDF of climate change. Historical observed data are used to assess model reliability in representing current climate, so that models with large biases are discounted. How well each model's future projection agrees with the ensemble consensus is also taken into account, rewarding the central tendencies and slightly discounting more extreme projections.

Temperature and Precipitation in 2100: Simulated Changes in Annual Averages. The range of uncertainty quantified in these PDFs is dependent on and limited by the specific emission scenario assumed and the set of GCMs used, which are thought of representing a fairly conservative set. Nonetheless, the climate models project a consistent warming on average from the present through 2025 and 2050 to a mean annual temperature increase on the order of about 3-4°C (6-8°F) in the year 2100 (Figure 23). It is perhaps worth observing in passing that the total worldwide warming during the ten thousand years of the Holocene period (i.e., since the end of the last Ice Age) was only slightly greater at approximately 4.5°C (about 9°F). With respect to moisture conditions, this analysis of twenty-one climate models indicated that the most likely projection for future precipitation is centered around the current average with equal probabilities for more/less precipitation (Figures 24 and 25).

---

[5] e.g., water quantity and quality issues, droughts, tropical storms

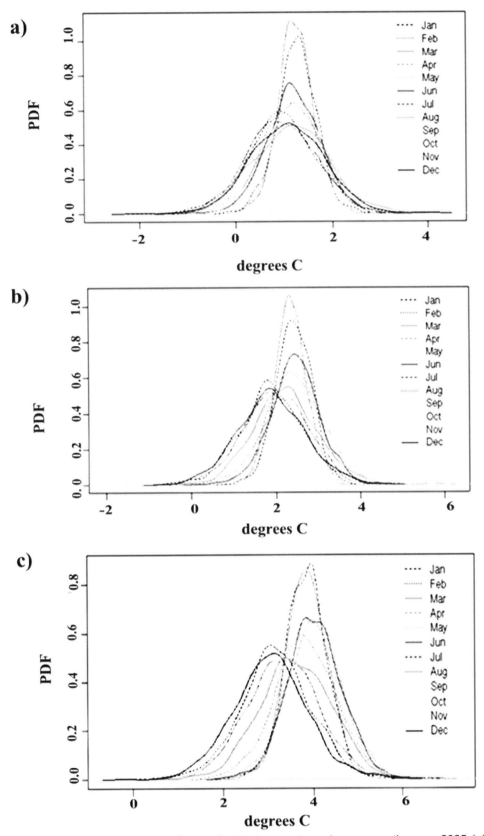

Figure 23. South Texas future climate: temperature change over the year 2025 (a), 2050 (b), and 2100(c), calculations by C. Tebaldi, NCAR 2006

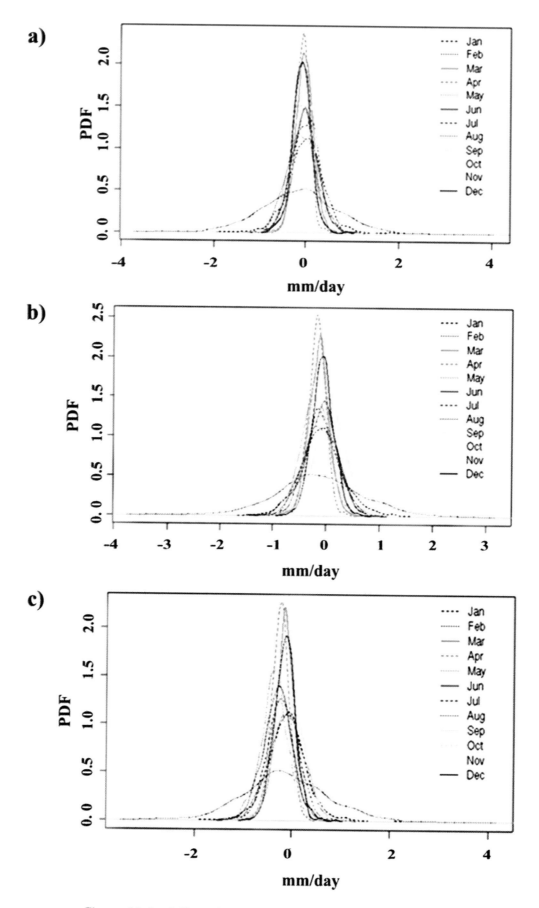

Figure 24. South Texas future climate: precipitation change (mm) over the year 2025 (a), 2050 (b), and 2100 (c), calculations by C. Tebaldi, NCAR 2006

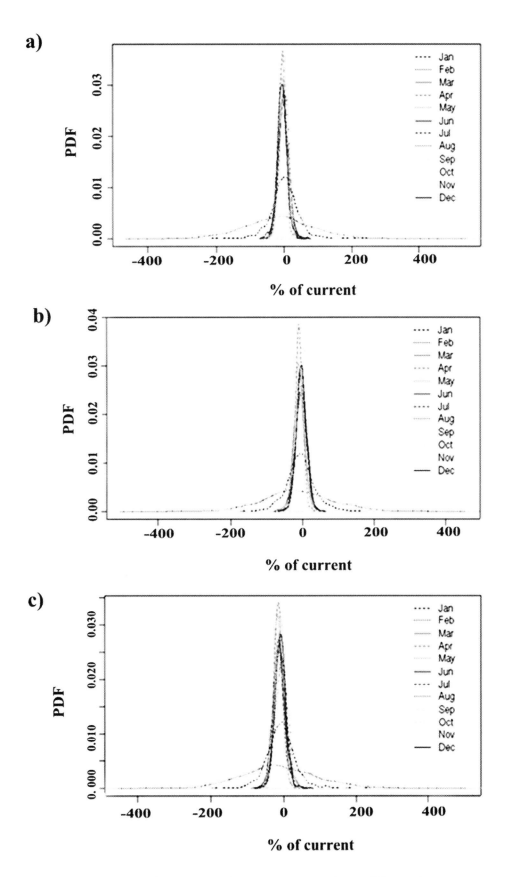

Figure 25. South Texas future climate:precipitation change (%) over the year
2025 (a), 2050 (b), and 2100 (c), calculations by C. Tebaldi, NCAR 20006

Changes in Precipitation Intensity and Sea Level: Likely 2100 Scenarios. An analysis of the changes in indices of climate extremes from climate-model output (Tebaldi et al. 2006). Five indices were examined related to changes in precipitation patterns. Four of these considered changes in intensity in various form and one addressed changes in the length of dry spells. For the area of South Texas the changes found were in the direction of *longer dry spells coupled with an increase in high-intensity precipitation events.* The climate models agreed on these changes, but only the change in dry spells was found to be statistically significant for a majority of models. In another recent study, focusing specifically on the "precipitation intensity index" (simply defined as the total annual precipitation divided by the number of wet days), she concluded that the general increase in water vapor and moisture convergence is responsible for a general increase in mean precipitation over high latitudes and in the tropics. In general, the mid-latitudes do not see a consistent change in mean precipitation, unless they are areas where changes in the circulation patterns are significant. South Texas is not one of those, but the significant change in dry spells (towards longer such spells) should safely imply that in a scenario where average precipitation does not show a significant change (as the models have suggested will be the case in southern Texas in 2100) the result will probably be episodes of larger intensity (Tebaldi 2006).

Finally, a word about sea level along the lower Texas coast seems appropriate to mention at least in passing, even though a "best-guess" estimate remains the state of the science at this juncture. Two scenarios that seem because of their massive implications for natural and human ecologies and economies deserving of consideration are the following:

1. The most likely rise in sea level due to global warming given the IPCC "business as usual" model assumptions (i.e., no drastic reduction in greenhouse gas emissions) is about 2 to 3 meters (6.6 to 9.8 ft) in the year 2100 (Hansen 2006);

2. A best-guess estimate of sea level rise at the start of the twenty-second century given more rapid disintegration of the Greenland and Antarctic ice sheets, e.g., the melting of the West Antarctic ice sheet, is about 6 meters (19.7 ft) (Hansen 2006).

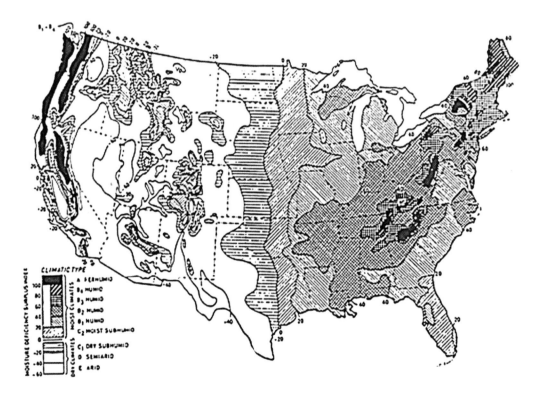

Figure 26. Moisture Regions of the U.S.: percent (Thornthwaite 1931, 1933, and 1948)

Toward 2100 Summary: The most logical interpretation of this analysis of our future regional climate using GCMs supports the conclusion that the most likely scenario for the late-twenty-first century climate of South Texas is that of an increasing reduction in water supply (i.e., higher temperatures + constant precipitation=greater moisture deficiencies), with the least likely scenario being increased water supplies, as well as longer dry spells and more high-intensity precipitation events. If correct, this scenario is unlikely to render the climate of South Texas any less problematic. For example, it suggests the possibility, perhaps even probability, that the existing regional climatic divides will move eastward by century's end (Figure 25), with eastern South Texas shifting from subhumid to semiarid and western South Texas shifting from semiarid to semi-desert.

Toward 2100: Examples of Potential Implications of the Simulated Climate Changes Global Warming and the Future of South Texas: What to Do?

"What should be done?" There is of course a difficult collective dimension to this question. On the one hand, if people of today choose to sacrifice some lifestyle to reduce greenhouse-gas emissions, their grandchildren or more likely their great-grandchildren, will inherit a world in which human-induced global warming will be less extreme than they would have been otherwise. On the other hand, the atmosphere is more like an aircraft carrier than a canoe. It does not turn on a dime. That means that those of living now who will incur the costs and inconveniences will not live long enough to enjoy any of the benefits. This is the sort of combination of immediate sacrifice for future benefit which has come to seem problematic for modern democratic societies.

Acknowledgements

This work was supported by a grant from the National Science Foundation to the The Frank H. Dotterweich College of Engineering at Texas A&M University-Kingsville and its Center of Research Excellence in Science and Technology-Research on Environmental Sustainability of Semi-Arid Coastal Areas (CREST-RESSACA). The authors wish to express their grateful appreciation for this support by the Foundation and Texas A&M University-Kingsville's CREST-RESSACA, without which it would not have been possible to conduct, or publish the results of, this research project.

Notes

The sections of this paper dealing with the twentieth century climate of South Texas represent an update of these previous publications:

- Norwine, Jim, Ralph Bingham, and Rosalia Vidal Zepeda. 1978. Twentieth Century Semiarid Climates and Climatic Fluctuations in Texas and Northeastern Mexico. *Journal of Arid Environments* 1:313-325.

- Norwine, Jim and Ralph Bingham 1986. Frequency and Severity of Droughts in South Texas: 1900-1983. *Livestock and Wildfire Management During Drought, 1986,* ed. R. Braun, Kingsville, TX: Caesar Kleberg Wildlife Research Institute, Texas A&I University.

- Le Houerou, H. and Jim Norwine. 1987. The Ecoclimatology of South Texas. *Arid Lands: Today and Tomorrow* eds. E. Whitehead et al. Boulder, CO: Westview Press. 417- 443

Parts of this paper have also been freely adapted from several of our other previous publications, including the following:

- Norwine, Jim et al. 1995. The Changing Climate of Texas: Predictability and Implications for the Future. *Cartographics* College Station, TX: Texas A&M University 138-154.

- Norwine, Jim and Jane Powley. 1992. Effects of Carbon Dioxide-Induced Global Warming on Water Budget in Southern Texas, *Managing Water Resources During Global Change.* American Water Resources Association 203-209.

- Norwine, Jim et al. 2006. The Climate of South Texas: Yes, It Will Continue to Keep the Riff-Raff Out! *The Journal of South Texas Studies.*

In a few instances data was severely restricted prior to 1930, in which case the temperature/precipitation averages and resulting plots were more heavily influenced by available data-records from the first-order stations, i.e., the Corpus Christi and San Antonio data-sets.

Literature Cited

Arnell, N. W. 1999. Climate Change and Global Water Resources. *Global Environmental Change* 9:S31-S49.

Carter, Douglas and John Mather. 1966. *Climatic Classification for Environmental Biology.* C.W. Thornthwaite Associates Laboratory of Climatology. Elmer, NJ: Publications in Climatology, 29(4)

Committee on the Science of Climate Change. 2001. *Climate Change Science: An Analysis of Some Key Questions.* National Washington, DC:Academy Press.

Gates, W. L., et al. 1996. Climate Models - Evaluation, in IPCC, 1996a. *Climate Change 1995 - The Science of Climate Change.* Contribution of Working Group I to the Second Assessment Report of the Intergovernmental Panel on Climate Change. Cambridge, UK: Cambridge University Press.

Giorgi, Filippo and Linda O. Mearns. 1991. Approaches to the Simulation of Regional Climate Change: A Review. *Reviews of Geophysics* 29(2):191-216.

Grotch, S. L. and M. C. MacCracken. 1991. The Use of General Circulation Models to Predict Regional Climatic Change. *Journal of Climate* 4: 286-303.

Hansen, J. 2001. Earth's Becoming a Greener Greenhouse. *Top Story: Goddard Space Flight Center* (September 4, 2001) www.gsfc.nasa.gov/topstory/20010904greenhouse.html/.

Hansen, J., L. Nazarenko, R. Ruedy, Mki. Sato, J. Willis, A. Del Genio, D. Koch, A. Lacis, K. Lo, S. Menon, T. Novakov, Ju. Perlwitz, G. Russell, G. A. Schmidt, and N. Tausnev. 2005a. Earth's energy imbalance: Confirmation and implications. *Science* 308:1431-1435, doi:10.1126/science.1110252

Hansen, J., Mki. Sato, R. Ruedy, L. Nazarenko, A. Lacis, G. A. Schmidt, G. Russell, I. Aleinov, M. Bauer, S. Bauer, N. Bell, B. Cairns, V. Canuto, M. Chandler, Y. Cheng, A. Del Genio, G. Faluvegi, E. Fleming, A. Friend, T. Hall, C. Jackman, M. Kelley, N. Y. Kiang, D. Koch, J. Lean, J. Lerner, K. Lo, S. Menon, R. L. Miller, P. Minnis, T. Novakov, V. Oinas, Ja. Perlwitz, D. Rind, A. Romanou, D. Shindell, P. Stone, S. Sun. N. Tausnev, D. Thresher, B. Wielicki, T. Wong, M. Yao, and S. Zhang. 2005. Efficacy of climate Forcings. *Journal of Geophysical Research* 110:D18104, doi: 10.1029/2005JD005776.

Hansen, J. E. 2005. A Slippery Slope: How Much Global Warming Constitutes "Dangerous Anthropogenic Interference"? An editorial essay. *Climate Change* 68:269-279, doi:10.1007/s10584-005-4135-0.

Hansen, J. 2006. Personal correspondence with senior author, May 11, 2006.

Intergovernmental Panel on Climate Change (IPCC). 2001. *Summary for Policy Makers, Climate Change 2001.* www.ipcc.ch. (At the same website see also the IPCC reports for 1995 and 2005).

Intergovernmental Panel on Climate Change (IPCC). 2001. *Climate Change 2001: The Scientific Basis.* eds. Houghton J. T., et al. Cambridge, UK: Cambridge University Press.

Intergovernmental Panel on Climate Change (IPCC) 2000. *IPCC Special Report on Emissions Scenarios.* Cambridge, UK: Cambridge University Press.

Jha, Alok. 2006. Forecast Puts Earth's Future Under a Cloud. *The Guardian Unlimited* (August 15, 2006) www.guardian.co.uk/science/story/0,,1844789,00.html/.

Johannessen, O. M. 2006. Arctic Climate—Will the Ice Disappear in This Century? *RTCC: Responding to Climate Change* (March 20, 2006) www.rtcc.org/dec04/NERSC-en.html/.

Johannessen, O. M., L. Bengtsson, M. W.Miles, S. I. Kusmina, V. A. Semenov, G. Alekseev, V. F. Zakharov, A. P. Hasselmann, L. P. Bobylev, L. H. Pettersson, and H. Cattle. 2004. Arctic Climate Change—Observed and Modeled Temperature and Sea Ice. *Tellus* 56A (4):328-341.

Karl, T. R., Susan J. Hassol, Christopher D. Miller, and William L. Murray, eds. 2006. *Temperature Trends in the Lower Atmosphere: Steps for Understanding and Reconciling Differences.* A Report by the Climate Change Science Program and the Subcommittee on Global Change Research, Washington, DC. http://www.climatescience.gov/Library/sap/sap1-1/finalreport/default.htm.

Karoly, D. J. 2003. Detection of Anthropogenic Climate Change in the North American Region. *AMS 14th Global Change Symposium*, Long Beach, California, Feb. 9-13, 2003.

National Academy of Sciences. 2001. Committee on the Science of Climate Change. *Climate Change Science: An Analysis of Some Key Questions* Washington, D.C: National Academy Press.

Meehl, G. A. and C. Tebaldi. 2004. More Intense, More Frequent and Longer Lasting Heat Waves in the 21st Century. *Science* 305:5686:994-997.

Meehl, G. A., C. Tebaldi and D. Nychka.2004a. Changes in Frost Days in Simulations of 21st Century Climate. *Climate Dynamics* 23(5):495-511.

Meehl, G. A., W. M. Washington, C. M. Ammann, J. A. Arblaster, T. M. Wigley, and C. Tebaldi. 2004b. Combinations of Natural and Anthropogenic Forcings in 20th Century Cimate. *Journal of Climate* 17(19):3721-3727.

Meehl, G. A., J. M. Arblaster, and C. Tebaldi. 2005. Understanding Future Patterns of Increased Precipitation Intensity in Climate Models. *Geophysics Research Letters* 32.

Meko, D., M. Hughes, and C. Stockton. 1991. Climate Change and Climate Variability: The Paleo Record. in National Research Council. *Managing Water Resources in the West under Conditions of Climate Uncertainty* Washington, DC: National Academy Press.

Nakicenovic, N. and R. Swart, eds. 2000. *Emission Scenarios. 2000: Special Report of the Intergovernmental Panel on Climate Change* Cambridge, UK: Cambridge University Press.

Nash, L. L. and P. H. Gleick. 1993. *The Colorado River Basin and Climatic Change: The Sensitivity of Streamflow and Water Supply to Variations in Temperature and Precipitation.* Report prepared for the U.S. Environmental Protection Agency, Office of Policy, Planning and Evaluation - Climate Change Division, EPA 230-R-93-009, Oakland, CA: Pacific Institute for Studies in Development, Environment, and Security.

National Assessment Synthesis Team (NAST). 2000. *Climate Change Impacts on the United States--Overview Report: The Potential Consequences of Climate Variability and Change* Cambridge, UK: Cambridge University Press, 158 pages http://www.usgcrp.gov/usgcrp/Library/nationalassessment/overview.htm.

Parallel IPCC reports: *Climate Change 2001: Impacts, Adaptation and Vulnerability - Contribution of Working Group II to the Intergovernmental Panel on Climate Change (IPCC) Third Assessment Report.*

Parallel IPCC Reports. 2001. *Climate Change 2001: Mitigation - Contribution of Working Group III* Intergovernmental Panel on Climate Change (IPCC) Third Assessment Report.

Rayner, N. A., et al. 2003. Global Analyses of Sea Surface Temperature, Sea Ice, and Night Marine Air Temperature since the late Nineteenth Century. *Journal of Geophys. Research* 108:4407, doi:10.1029/2002JD002670.

Stahle, David and Malcolm Cleaveland. 1988. Texas Drought History Reconstructed and Analyzed from 1698 to 1980. *Journal of Climate* 11:59-74.

Stott, Peter, G. S. Jones, and J. F. B. Mitchell 2003. Do Models Underestimate the Solar Contribution to Recent Climate Change? *Journal of Climate*, 15 (December 2003): 4079-4093.

Summary for Policy Makers, Climate Change 2001: The Scientific Basis. Summary for Policymakers and Technical Summary of the Working Group I Report. Cambridge University Press, Also available at http://www.ipcc.ch.

Tebaldi, C., L. O. Mearns, D. Nychka, and R. L. Smith. 2004. Regional Probabilities of Precipitation Change: A Bayesian Analysis of Multimodel Simulations. *Geophysical Research Letters* 31.

Tebaldi, C., K. Hayhoe , J. M. Arblaster, and G. A. Meehl. 2006. Going to the Extremes: An Intercomparison of Model-simulated Historical and Future Changes in Extreme Events. *Climatic Change* 79.

Tebaldi, C., K. Hayhoe, J. M. Arblaster, and G. A. Meehl. 2006. Going to the Extremes: An Intercomparison of Model-simulated Hstorical and Fture Canges in Etreme Eents. *Climatic Change* forthcoming.

Trenberth, K. E., A. Dai, R. M. Rasmussen, and D. B. Parsons. 2003. The Changing Character of Precipitation. *Bulletin of the American Meteorological Society* 84(9):1205–1217.

Thornthwaite, C. W. 1931.The Climates of North America According to a New Classification. *Geographical Review* 21:633-655. Separate map at 1:20,000,000.

Thornthwaite, C. W. 1933. The Climates of the Earth. *Geographical Review* 23:433-440. Separate map at 1:77,000,000.

Thornthwaite, C.W. 1948. An Approach Towards a Rational Classification of Climate. *Geographical Review* 38:55-94.

Tourpali, K, C. J. E. Schuurmans, R. van Dorland, B. Steil, C. Brühl, and E. Manzini. 2005. Solar Cycle Modulation of the Arctic Oscillation in a Chemistry-climate Model *Geophys. Research Lett* Vol. 32(September 3, 2005):L17803, doi:10.1029/2005GL023509, September 3, 2005.

Trewartha, Glenn T. 1968. *An Introduction to Climate* New York: McGraw-Hill.

Zwiers and Zhang. 2003. Towards Regional Climate Change Detection. *Journal of Climate* 16:793-797.

3

South Texas Climate 2100: Coastal Impacts

Paul A. Montagna, James C. Gibeaut , and John W. Tunnell, Jr.,

Issues

There will be considerable challenges and consequences involving climate change, particularly sea-level rise, during the next century along the South Texas coast. A rising global sea-level will have a disproportionate effect in South Texas due to the flat topography (Twilley et al. 2001). As shorelines move landward, marine and estuarine habitats will change or migrate also. Other probable climate change impacts will include: alterations in freshwater inflows from rivers; changes in estuarine ecosystem functioning; more frequent or longer-lasting droughts; increased incidence of extreme salt concentrations in some coastal ecosystems; changes in various kinds of habitats (increases in some, and decreases in others); and, further reductions in certain estuarine-dependent species: e.g. oysters, blue crabs, shrimp.

Scientists have two primary methods for forecasting these future changes or impacts. One method is to analyze and study similar conditions in the past and projecting those conditions on future coastal landscapes. For example, when conditions in South Texas were considerably wetter as evidenced by *Rangia* clams on the Nueces Delta or worm tube rocks in Baffin Bay; or when conditions were drier, like the 1950s, when vast sand dunes occupied large portions of the back side of barrier islands. Another method is in analyzing large data sets of the past and projecting those into the future using conceptual models or scenarios of future conditions. Neither of these approaches can predict exact conditions, but people living in the area, particularly those responsible for future planning (city, county, state, and federal managers or trustees), should be aware of future possible consequences.

An increasing body of literature is available to evaluate potential climatic changes and sea-level rise impacts on the Texas coast:

- sea-level rise impacts on salt marsh and bay productivity (Zimmerman et al. 1991);
- estuarine habitats and freshwater inflow (Longley 1995);
- hypoxia in coastal waters (Justic 1996);
- potential risks of climate change to Gulf Coast ecosystems and the goods and services they provide (Twilley et al. 2001; Ning et al. 2003 a and b);
- status and historical trends in seagrass habitats (Pulich and Blair 1997),
- wind-tidal flats (Withers and Tunnell 1998),
- other estuarine and coastal habitats (White et al. 1998);
- status and trends of wetlands and aquatic habitats on Texas barrier islands and adjacent bay systems (White et al. 2002, and 2006); and,
- impacts to ecosystems and social systems (Alvarez et al. 2006).

Current Coastal Landscape

There are seven major estuarine systems along 600 kilometers (373 miles) of coastline (Figure 1, Longley 1994). All seven Texas estuaries have similar geomorphic structure and physiography. Barrier islands are parallel to the mainland along the coast, and lagoons are found between the islands and mainland. The lagoons are interrupted with drowned river valleys that form the bay and estuarine systems. There are Gulf inlets through the barrier islands, which connect the sea with the lagoon behind the island. The lagoon opens to a large primary bay, and there is a constriction between the primary bay and the smaller secondary bay. Most bays are fed by just one or two rivers draining watersheds. The river generally flows into the secondary bay. Primary bays have greater marine influence and secondary bays have greater freshwater influence.

The Texas coast is bounded by Sabine River (border to Louisiana) in the northeast and the Rio Grande (border with Mexico) in the southwest. The major bay-estuarine systems are the Sabine-Neches Estuary, Trinity-San Jacinto Estuary, Lavaca-Colorado Estuary, Guadalupe Estuary, Mission-Aransas Estuary, Nueces Estuary, and Laguna Madre Estuary. Laguna Madre is actually two different systems: Upper Laguna Madre/Baffin Bay and Lower Laguna Madre. Texas follows the traditional system of naming an estuary for the river(s) that dilute sea water (Longely 1994). In NOAA publications (e.g., Orlando et al. 1993), these systems are named after the primary bay: Sabine Lake, Galveston Bay, Matagorda Bay, San Antonio Bay, Aransas Bay, Corpus Christi Bay, and Laguna Madre, respectively. There are also three riverine estuaries, the Brazos River, San Bernard River, and the Rio Grande, which flow directly into the Gulf of Mexico.

Freshwater wetlands and lower salinity brackish-salt marshes and oyster reefs are common in the north and higher salinity seagrass beds and wind-tidal flats are common to the south. In the Texas Coastal Bend, Corpus Christi lies at the approximate boundary where precipitation exceeds evaporation to the north and evaporation exceeds precipitation to the south (Table 1). Hence, Laguna Madre is a higher salinity lagoon, containing over 80% of Texas seagrasses (Pulich and Blair 1997) and over 80% of Texas wind-tidal flats (Withers and Tunnell 1998).

Table 1. Areal extent of selected Texas coastal habitats (mi²) during the mid-1950s. Note the increases in coverage of marsh habitat and oyster reefs from south to north along the decreasing bay salinity gradient, and the increases in seagrasses and wind-tidal flats in the drier south Texas coast.

Habitat	Laguna Madre	Nueces	Mission-Aransas	Guadalupe	Lavaca -Colorado	Trinity - San Jacinto	Sabine-Neches
Fresh Marsh	16.2	9	5.7	17.7	21.4	19.4	26.6
Swamp	0	0	0.3	1.5	0.1	34.6	36.3
Salt-Brackish Marsh	2.3	7	25.2	27.9	29.6	116.6	118
Wind- Tidal Flat	344	19.2	23.4	12.4	5.6	6.5	0
Seagrass	220	12.4	9.5	8.4	5.7	8	0
Beach-Barrier	156.1	17.3	23.6	25.9	27.9	61	14.3
Oyster Reef	0	3.2	13.6	18.7	8.4	88.8	0
Open Bay	266	157.6	184.6	206.9	366.1	493.6	49
Dredge Material	30.7	9.7	3.9	4.7	10.7	11.2	16.7

Adapted from Brown et al. (1976, 1977 and 1978), McGowen (1976), and Longley (1995).

Sea-Level and Shoreline Change

Past and Ongoing Shoreline Change

Most of the sandy Gulf of Mexico shoreline of South Texas has probably been retreating for several thousand years and definitely since the mid to late 1800s when sufficiently accurate shoreline maps were constructed for comparison with today's maps. An analysis of multiple Gulf of Mexico shorelines from 1930 to 2000 and from the Colorado River to the US–Mexico border shows that 56% of the shoreline retreated at a mean rate of 2.2 meters/year (7.22 feet/year), 36% remained essentially stable, and only 8% advanced seaward. Advancing shoreline sections were associated with impoundment of sand by jetties or spit progradation caused by engineering alterations affecting Pass Cavallo. A section a few miles long in the central Padre Island area also advanced because of the natural convergence of littoral drift.

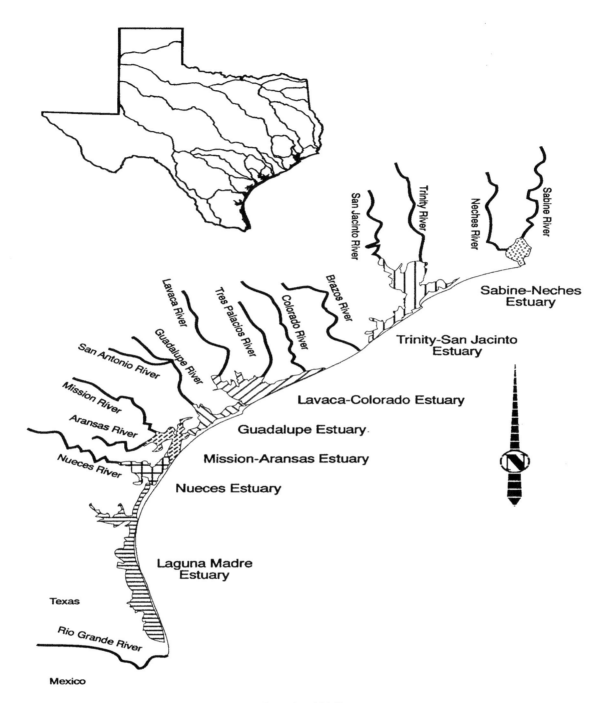

Figure 1. Location of Texas Estuaries (Longley 1994)

Bay shorelines have been retreating for at least ten thousand years as sea level rose from the lowstand of eighteen thousand years ago and flooded paleoriver channels running through the bays. Inundation, waves, and tidal action eroded river banks, and the resulting shoreline retreat largely shaped the bays as they exist today. Generally these bay shorelines continue to retreat with the erosion of marshes and flats, clay bluffs, sandy slopes, and sand and shell beaches. In some areas, extensive shore-protection structures such as rip rap and bulkheads have been installed. Paine and Morton (1993) determined an average retreat rate for the Copano, Aransas, and Redfish Bay systems of 0.24 m/yr (0.79 ft/yr) from 1930 through 1982. In Baffin Bay, most of the shoreline retreated from 1941 through 1995 (Gibeaut and Tremblay 2003).

Changing sea level relative to the land (relative sea-level change) and the increase and decrease in sand supply to the coast causes shorelines to retreat or advance over a period of a hundred years or more (Bruun 1962; Gibeaut and Tremblay 2003). The rise in relative sea level during the last one hundred years along the South Texas coast has moved the Gulf and bay shorelines by inundation and by shifting the erosive energy of waves and currents landward. This has happened because, overall the rate of new sediment delivered to the littoral zone has not been sufficient to stem the effects of relative sea-level rise. Localized exceptions to this are where rivers form deltas at the heads of the bays, such as the Nueces and Mission Deltas; and where creeks erode bluffs and enter the bays (Morton and Paine 1984; Paine and Morton 1993); and where dunes have migrated and advanced the shoreline (Prouty and Prouty 1989; Gibeaut and Tremblay 2003). Because of this sediment deficit and the low-lying and gently sloping shores of much of the South Texas coast, relative sea-level rise has had and will continue to have a profound effect on coastal habitats. Increases in the rate of global sea-level rise, as projected by global climate modeling (Intergovernmental Panel on Climate Change [IPCC 2007]), and coastal development will very likely result in further decreases of coastal wetland habitats.

Relative Sea-Level Change

Relative sea-level rise along the South Texas coast is caused by natural and human-induced land surface-subsidence and a global rise in ocean level. Global sea level is rising primarily through addition of water to the oceans by melting continental ice and to a lesser degree, through thermal expansion of ocean water (Miller and Douglas 2004), both of which are caused by global warming. Tide-gauge records in South Texas, which include the effects of land subsidence, show that relative sea level has risen at a rate of 4.6 mm/yr (0.18 in/yr) at Rockport since 1948, 2.05 mm/yr (0.08 in/yr) at Port Mansfield since 1963, and 3.44 mm/yr (0.14 in/yr) at South Padre Island since 1958 (Zervas 2001). Douglas (1991) considered tide gauges from around the world and, after accounting for vertical land movements, determined that global sea level from the late nineteenth through the late twentieth century rose at a rate of only 1.8 mm/yr (0.07 in/yr). Land subsidence rates can be estimated for tide gauge locations by subtracting 1.8 mm/yr (0.07 in/yr) from the relative sea-level rise rate recorded by the gauge. This calculation illustrates that land subsidence is an important component of relative sea-level rise in South Texas.

The South Texas coastal plain was built by an accumulation of alluvial, estuarine, coastal, and deeper marine sediments over the last hundred and fifty million years. This stack of mud and sand is 10- to 15-km thick (6.21 to 9.32 mi) (Antoine and Gilmore 1970) and is compacting under its own weight at a long-term (hundred thousand years) rate of about 0.05 mm/yr (0.001 in/yr) (Paine 1993). Higher rates of natural compaction, however, are likely occurring over the last ten thousand years as the sediments deposited during the latest transgression of the sea compact. Areas along the South Texas coast with these relatively thick and unconsolidated Holocene sediments are the barrier islands, bay margins, and estuarine deltas, which contain important habitats highly sensitive to sea-level fluctuations. Meckel et al. (2006) used a sediment compaction model to show statistically that the amount of compaction is generally greater in areas with thicker and more rapidly deposited sediments. Using Meckel's results and stratigraphy of Mustang Island (Simms et al. 2006) and the Nueces Delta (Brown et al. 1976), the likely natural rate of subsidence of South Texas barrier islands and modern deltas ranges from 1 to 5 mm/yr (0.04 to 0.20 in/yr).

Additional land subsidence is caused by groundwater withdrawal and oil and gas production, which decrease pore pressures in underlying sediments, allowing further compaction. Ratzlaff (1980) compared releveling surveys for various periods from 1917 through 1975 and observed locally high land subsidence rates of as much as 49 mm/yr (1.93 in/yr), such as at the Saxet oil and gas field southwest of Nueces Bay. Highest rates correlated with oil, gas, and groundwater production. By combining tide-gauge and releveling data, Paine (1993) estimated Texas coastal subsidence rates of 3 to 7 mm/yr (0.12 to 0.28 in/yr). Sharp et al. (1991) and Paine (1993) hypothesized that regional depressurization of petroleum reservoirs was the cause of historical subsidence rates being much higher than geologically long-term rates. Morton et al. (2006) provided evidence of hydrocarbon production causing regional land subsidence and associated wetland loss in the Mississippi Delta and the upper Texas coast regions.

It is clear that the rate of relative sea-level rise has and will continue to vary along the South Texas coast because of natural and human-induced land subsidence. It is also clear that the magnitude of the subsidence will continue to contribute a significant portion of relative sea-level rise, even with projected increases in global sea-level rise caused by global warming. Furthermore, just as the rate of global sea-level rise is expected to increase with further global warming, we can expect to experience at least local increases in land subsidence as more hydrocarbon and groundwater extraction occurs. Because of the implications for the sustainability of coastal habitats, determining the patterns, causes, and possible mitigation strategies of natural and man-induced coastal land subsidence should be a priority for future research.

Relative Sea-Level and Shoreline Change Projections

The IPCC (2007) report provides model projections for global sea-level rise based on six greenhouse-gas and aerosol-emission scenarios. The range in the amount of projected global sea-level rise by 2099 relative to the average from

1980 through 1999 is 0.18 to 0.59 m (0.59 to 1.93 ft). After adding estimates for local land subsidence, the amount of projected relative sea-level rise by the year 2100 is 0.46 to 0.87 m (1.51 to 2.85 ft) at Rockport, 0.20 to 0.61 m (0.66 to 2.00 ft) at Port Mansfield, and 0.34 to 0.75 m (1.12 to 2.46 ft) at South Padre Island. These amounts will likely be greater in areas with relatively thick Holocene deposits filling paleoriver channels and tidal inlets, such as along barrier islands and modern deltas at the heads of bays (e.g. Nueces River Delta), and they may be much higher where subsidence caused by groundwater and hydrocarbon extraction occurs.

Depositional subenvironments of barrier islands and bay margins are the substrates for various types of aquatic, wetland, and upland habitats. These subenvironments and associated habitats are closely linked to elevation relative to sea level through the processes that form and maintain them. On the low-lying, sandy, barrier islands of the microtidal (tide range 0.6 m (1.97 ft) on the open coast and less than 0.3 m (0.98 ft) in the bays) South Texas coast, a rise of just 0.1 m (0.32 ft) in relative sea level can cause conversion of fringing low marshes and flats to open water and seagrass beds, and usually dry high marshes and flats to usually wet low marshes and flats (Gibeaut et al. 2003).

Mustang Island is a barrier island at the mouth of Corpus Christi Bay (Figure 1). Most of the island, except for the tallest foredunes, is less than 3 m (9.84 ft) above sea level, which is typical for the barrier islands along the South Texas coast. Inundation of Mustang Island by relative sealevel-rise amounts projected for 2100 are depicted in Figure 2. Even a rise of just 0.46 m (1.51 ft) will cause lateral shifts of 1 to 2 km (0.62 to 1.24 mi) of bay-side wetland environments. The upper bound rise amount of 0.87 m (2.85 ft) will narrow the upland areas of the island to a width less than 200 m (656.17 ft) in places and flood central portions of the City of Port Aransas on the north end of the island.

Actual shoreline retreat and loss of wetland areas on South Texas barrier islands will depend not just on relative sea-level rise but also on

1) whether vertical sediment accretion can keep up with the rise,
2) whether adjacent upland slopes are gentle enough for wetlands to migrate landward,
3) whether development obstructs the upward/landward migration of wetlands, and
4) the severity of erosion by waves and currents at the edge of marshes and flats.

Given the observed conversion of tidal flats to open water and seagrass beds and the migration of marshes into higher areas since the 1950s on Mustang and adjacent islands (White et al. 2006), it is unlikely that vertical accretion will offset the effects of an increase in the rate of relative sea-level rise. Upland slopes increase toward the core of the islands, tempering the amount of new marsh that can develop. It is very likely that future development will obstruct new marsh creation, such as occurred at the Padre Isles development beginning in the 1970s (White et al. 2006). Erosion of the outer edges of marshes and flats since the 1930s has caused shoreline retreat in the range of 0.5 to 2.5 m/yr (1.64 to 8.20 ft/yr) along most of the Mustang Island bay shoreline (Morton and Paine 1984; Williams 1999). Erosion by waves may increase as higher water level decreases the amount of wave shoaling and extends wave energy farther landward.

As sealevel rises and barrier islands become narrower, large storms will eventually breach, washover, and transport sand landward into the bays. This process is already happening along low and narrow portions of the South Texas coast, such as Corpus Christi and Newport Passes during Hurricane Beulah in 1967 (Davis et al. 1973) (Figure 2) and along South Padre Island during Hurricane Bret in 1999 (Figure 3). Furthermore, increasing aridity, which climate models predict for this region, has the potential to reduce stabilizing dune vegetation and cause more active dune migration and blowouts, as were observed on north Padre Island and Mustang Island during the drought period of the 1950s (White et al. 1978; Prouty and Prouty 1989). Hurricane intensities have increased recently and may continue to increase with warming of sea-surface temperatures (Emanuel 2005). Hence, rising sea level, increasing aridity, and increasing storm intensity will drive the South Texas barrier islands toward narrower, lower-lying islands that are more frequently washed over and severed by tropical storms similar to present-day Matagorda Peninsula, Texas (Figure 4). Eventually, depending on the actual rate of relative sea-level rise, portions of the South Texas barrier island chain will be destroyed, a scenario similar to the near demise of the Chandeleur Islands in Louisiana following recent hurricanes.

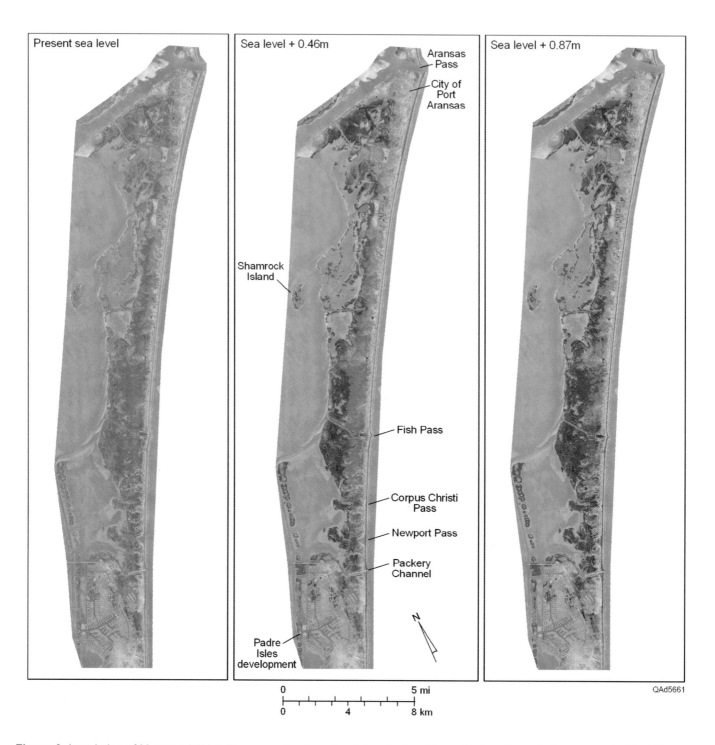

Figure 2. Inundation of Mustang Island. The amounts of sea-level rise depicted here (darker blue color) are expected in 100 years when combining local subsidence estimates with the lower and upper ranges of global sea-level rise projections presented in the IPCC (2007) report. This map was created using aerial photography draped on a high-resolution, lidar-derived digital elevation model. Lidar data acquisition and processing were performed by the Bureau of Economic Geology, The University of Texas at Austin in 2005.

Figure 3. Looking towards Laguna Madre at hurricane washover channels on Padre Island, Texas about 4 km (2.49 mi) north of Mansfield Pass. Hurricane Bret formed these channels when it struck on August 22, 1999. More than a dozen other former washover channels were reactivated by Bret. Darker blue indicates sea-level rise flooded areas.

Figure 4. Rising sea level, increased storm intensity, and increased aridity will drive the South Texas barrier islands towards narrower, lower-lying islands that are completely washed over and severed by tropical storms as shown here by present-day Matagorda Peninsula, Texas.

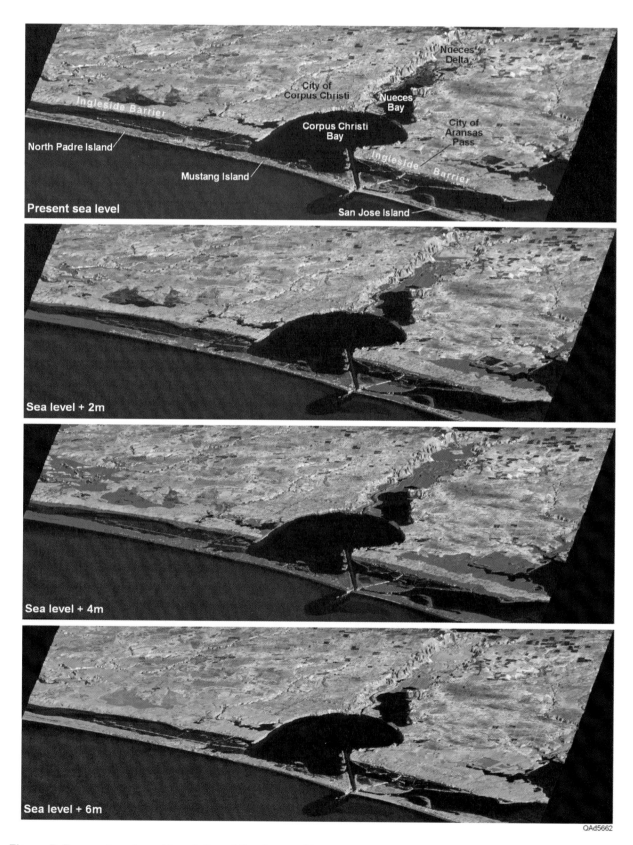

Figure 5. Perspective view of inundation of the Corpus Christi Bay area by sea-level rise. These scenarios are reflective of polar ice sheet melting and destabilization triggered by global warming. Topographic relief is vertically exaggerated six times.

potential changes in polar ice-sheet flow as global warming proceeds. Recent observations of ice-sheet changes suggest the possibility of large contributions to sea-level rise from the flow of Greenland and Antarctic glaciers into the oceans (Rignot and Kanagaratnam 2006; Shepherd and Wingham 2007). Overpeck et al. (2006) compared hundred-year global temperature projections in the *IPCC Third Assessment Report* (2001) with climatic and sea-level conditions during the last interglacial period about 130,000 years ago. During that time, polar temperatures were 3 to 5°C (5.4 to 9°F) higher than now, causing polar ice to retreat and contribute to sealevel 4 to more than 6 m (13.12 to more than 19.69 ft) higher than today. This amount of warming is within the range projected during the next hundred years by IPCC modeling studies. Therefore, increases in sealevel caused by melting polar ice may be expected to proceed for centuries resulting in sea-level rise of several meters and sea-level rise rates twice those projected in the IPCC (2007) report (Overpeck et al. 2006).

Figure 5 illustrates how a sea-level rise of 2, 4, and 6 m (6.56, 13.12, and 19.69 ft) would each inundate the Corpus Christi Bay area. Today's barrier islands would be completely submerged with a rise of less than 4 m (13.12 ft). The lower Nueces Delta would be submerged with a 2-m rise (6.56 ft), and the entire delta and lower river valley would be submerged with a 6-m rise (19.69 ft). Pleistocene bluffs and the relict Pleistocene delta-plain surface more than 6 m (19.69 ft) high confine the sea around the upper portions of Corpus Christi and Nueces bays and the Nueces River Valley. The Ingleside Barrier (Figure 5) is a relict barrier-strandplain system deposited about 120,000 years ago during the last interglacial period when sea level was 5 to 8 m (16.40 to 26.25 ft) higher than today (Wilkinson et al. 1975; Brown et al. 1976; Paine 1993). Even though the Ingleside Barrier has probably subsided several meters since its formation (Paine 1993), it is still emergent at elevated sea levels and may serve as the core for a future barrier-island system. It is important to note that simply raising the ocean level, as in Figures 5 and 6, does not reveal a realistic shape for the future shoreline because waves and currents will redistribute the sediments during the rise and constantly reshape the shoreline, with a tendency to smooth it.

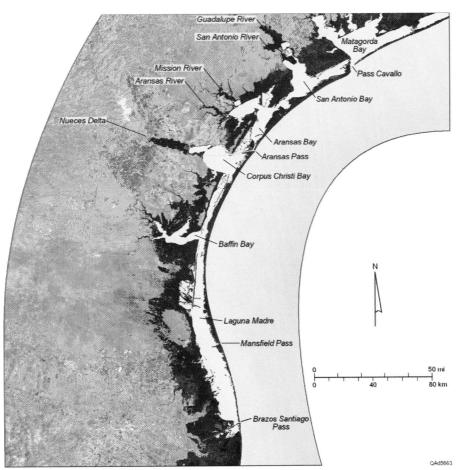

Figure 6. Inundation of land if the level of the sea were to rise 6 m (19.69 ft) above present level. Lighter blue shows the present bays and lagoons and the darker blue depicts inundated areas. This scenario is reflective of polar ice sheet melting and destabilization triggered by global warming during the next 100 years resulting in sea level rise rates of 10 mm/yr or more for centuries. Constant redistribution of sediments by waves and currents during sea-level rise would tend to smooth the shoreline, but that process is not reflected in this map.

Figure 6 depicts inundation of the South Texas coast if sea level were to rise 6 m (19.69 ft). In this scenario, the barrier islands are completely inundated, and the sea advances about 20 km (12.43 mi) inland from the bay margins except where sufficiently high Pleistocene bluffs and uplands exist. River valleys and deltas at the heads of secondary bays are flooded. White et al. (2002) showed that vertical accretion rates on the Nueces Delta are less than the rate of relative sea-level rise today. It is unlikely that vertical accretion rates will be sufficient to maintain wetlands on the South Texas deltas if relative sea-level rise rates increase to 10 mm/yr (0.39 in/yr) or more, as would happen in the Figure 6 scenario. If polar ice-sheet destabilization should occur, therefore, we can expect massive losses of critical wetland habitat in the bays.

Ecosystem Changes

Freshwater Inflow and Estuarine Functioning

The estuaries of Texas are remarkably hydrologically diverse in spite of similar geomorphology. This is due to a climatic gradient, which influences freshwater inflow to estuaries. The gradient of decreasing rainfall, and concomitant freshwater inflow, from northeast to southwest, is the most distinctive feature of the coastline (Table 2). Along this gradient, rainfall decreases by a factor of two, but inflow balance decreases by almost two orders of magnitude. Inflow balance is the sum of freshwater inputs (gaged, modeled runoff, direct precipitation, plus return flows) minus the outputs (diversions and evaporation). The net effect is a gradient with estuaries with similar physical characteristics but a declining salinity gradient.

Table 2. Climatic gradient in Texas estuaries. Listed from north to south: area at mean low tide (Diener 1975), average annual precipitation (1951-1980; Larkin and Bomar 1983), average annual freshwater inflow balance (1941-1999; Texas Water Development Board http://www.twdb.state.tx.us/data/bays_estuaries/bays_estuary _toc.htm), average salinity (Orlando et al. 1993), and average annual commercial harvest (1962-1998; Texas Parks and Wildlife Department 1988, Robinson et al. 2000).

Estuary	Area (km^2)	Rainfall (cm y^{-1})	Inflow (10^6 m^3 y^{-1})	Salinity (ppt)	Commercial Harvest Finfish (10^3 kg y^{-1})	Commercial Harvest Shellfish (10^3 kg y^{-1})
Sabine-Neches	183	142	16,897	8	3	341
Trinity-San Jacinto	1,416	112	14,000	16	176	4352
Lavaca-Colorado	1,158	102	3,801	18	59	2531
Guadalupe	551	91	2,664	16	63	1846
Mission-Aransas	453	81	265	15	140	1947
Nueces	433	76	298	23	173	840
Laguna Madre	1,139	69	-893	36	677	163

Freshwater inflow patterns appear to group into four distinct climatic subregions, which vary by about an order of magnitude each (Figure 7). The northeastern most subregion is composed of the Sabine-Neches Estuary (containing Sabine Lake) and the Trinity-San Jacinto Estuary (containing Galveston Bay). This northeastern subregion has the highest rainfall and inflow balance greater than 10^{10} m^3 y^{-1}. The next three climatic subregions form the largest area and contain five estuaries linked by large lagoons, extending from the Colorado River to the Rio Grande. The most well known lagoonal estuary is Laguna Madre. The climatic subregions are distinct in several ways. Most important is a lack of connection between the watersheds, thus each bay system is fed by different rivers. The Intracoastal Water Way provides a man-made, dredged channel linking all subregions. The Lavaca-Colorado Estuary (containing Matagorda Bay) and Guadalupe Estuary (containing San Antonio Bay) have an average inflow rate of about 10^9 m^3 y^{-1}. The Mission-Aransas Estuary (containing Aransas Bay) and Nueces Estuary (containing Corpus Christi Bay) have an average inflow rate of about 10^8 m^3 y^{-1}. Laguna Madre is a negative estuary because evaporation exceeds inputs and has an average negative inflow rate of about 10^8 m^3 y^{-1}. Thus the region spans positive, neutral and negative estuaries.

There is also a concomitant gradient of different timing of peak inflow events (Figure 8). The northern estuaries

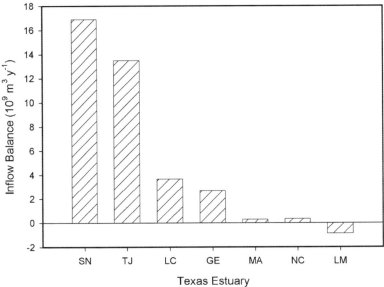

Figure 7. Averaage annual inflow balance from 1941-1994 in Texas estuaries from northeast to southwest. SN=Sabine-Neches Estuary, TJ=Trinity-San Jacinto Estuary, LC=Lavaca-Colorado Estuary, GE=Guadalupe Estuary, MA=Mission-Aransas Estuary, NC=Nueces Estuary, and LM=Laguna Madre Estuary

receive peak inflow during the spring, the central estuaries are bimodal receiving peak inflows during the spring and fall, and the southern most estuaries receive peak inflows during the fall. These distinct patterns are very important ecologically, because growth, reproduction, and migration of many species is keyed to seasonal events. The timing and magnitude of inundation is believed to regulate finfish and shellfish production (Texas Department Water Resources 1982). The differences within and among the subregions and estuaries of Texas provides a sufficiently broad scale to examine effects of climate change and variability on ecological processes.

The latitudinal gradient of decreasing inflow into estuaries regulates salinity. As well as a latitudinal climatic gradient, there is a longitudinal salinity gradient within each estuary. The salinity gradient within and among the estuaries has already been demonstrated to regulate the infaunal molluscan community (Montagna and Kalke 1995). There are also salinity gradients within the estuaries from the river mouth to the sea, which influences the zonation of communities found within the estuaries (Kalke and Montagna 1991; Montagna and Kalke 1992; 1995). The interactions among the geophysical factors of climate, estuarine physiography and diversity of habitat types in the Gulf of Mexico are factors that influence diversity of the region.

Another characteristic of Texas estuaries is the extreme year-to-year variability in inflow[1] (Figure 9). Consequently, salinity gradients within estuaries vary from year-to-year. The southwestern estuaries in particular appear to be in a nearly

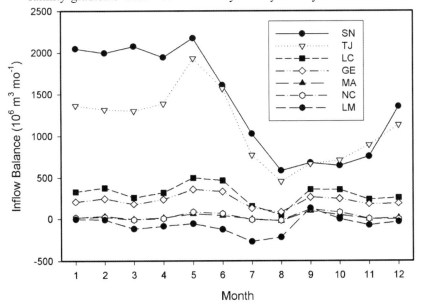

desert climate that is punctuated by flood events. The floods are caused by tropical storms or larger global climate patterns. The El Niño Southern Oscillation (ENSO) has a strong influence on inflow to Texas estuaries. The Southern Oscillation Index (SOI)[2] is negative during El Niño events. There is an inverse correlation between SOI and total inflow to the Texas coast (-0.14, p = 0004). The inverse correlation between smoothed SOI and smoothed total inflow to the Texas coast is strong (-0.47, p < 0001), but inflow is always highest when the SIO is negative (Figure 10). The ENSO phenomenon is only one climactic factor affecting inflow. Inflow is also influenced by tropical waves, which affect the coast from the east.

The importance of ENSO events on driving regional-scale climatic variability and salinity structure in Texas estuaries is now reasonable well understood (Tolan 2007). The

Figure 8. Average monthly inflow balance (1941 - 1994) in Texas estuaries. SN=Sabine-Neches Estuary, TJ=Trinity-San Jacinto Estuary, LC=Lavaca-Colorado Estuary, GE=Guadalupe Estuary, MA=Mission-Aransas Estuary, NC=Nueces Estuary, and LM=Laguna Madre Estuary.

[1] http://hyper20.twdb.state.tx.us/data/bays_estuaries/hydrologypage.html
[2] http://www.cgd.ucar.edu/cas/catalog/climind/soi.html

ENSO signals are correlated to salinity structure within Texas estuaries within four to six months. During El Niño events, salinities in Texas estuaries decrease because of increased freshwater flows to the coasts. During La Niña periods, salinities increase because of the drier climatic conditions. These cycles occur with a periodicity of 3.55, 5.33, and 10.67 years. The ENSO is dominated by the 3.55- and 5.33-year periods and the 10.67-year period is defined by the Pacific Decadal Oscillation

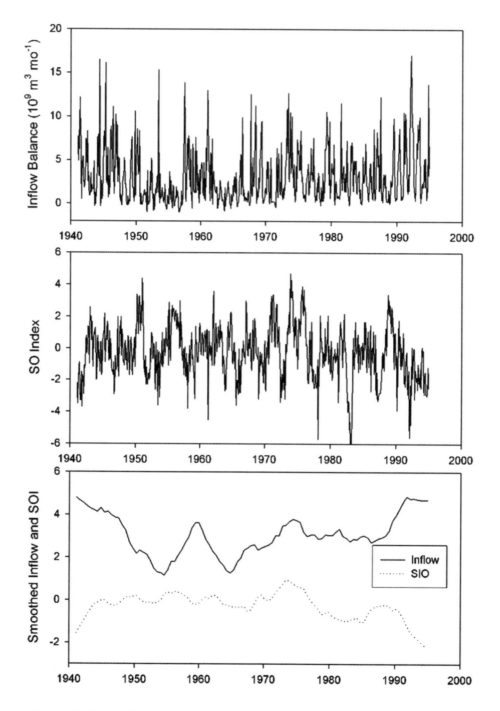

Figure 9. Total inflow of Texas Coast and Southern Oscillation Index (SOI). Bottom panel contains trends smoothed (using polynomial regression and weights computed from the Gaussian density).

The Texas coast is likely an ideal area to study climate change effects on estuaries, because it already is a natural experiment. There is physical similarity among Texas estuaries, each is simple draining only one or two watersheds, and they lie in a climatic gradient that is influenced by large-scale climate patterns in the Pacific and Atlantic Oceans. Being semi-arid and semi-tropical, small changes in global temperature will likely have large effects. For example, there has already been a 1.4°C (2.52°F) rise in surface temperatures of Corpus Christi Bay between 1982 and 2002, which correlates with a decrease in surface water oxygen content by 1.2 mg/L ((Applebaum et al. 2005). Further, it is simple to pose hypotheses, e.g., drier conditions will result in estuaries more like the southwestern estuaries, and wetter conditions will result in estuaries more like those to the northeast. It will be possible to design stratified sampling programs where statistical control can be used on confounding factors, e.g., watershed drainage basins, anthropogenic inputs, Gulf of Mexico exchange, specific habitats, circulation patterns, and alterations by man.

Habitat Change

Several federal and state agencies are charged with tracking or monitoring the environment along the Texas coast.

- The National Oceanic and Atmospheric Administration (NOAA) monitors estuarine-dependent species and their habitats.
- Texas Parks and Wildlife Department (TPWD) monitors coastal fisheries and related species,
- Texas General Land Office (TGLO) maintains and operates many coastal programs and is in charge of all Texas coastal submerged lands,
- Texas Commission on Environmental Quality (TCEQ) monitors air and water quality along the coast,
- Texas Water Development Board (TWDB) conducts research on freshwater inflows and impacts to Texas estuaries, and
- the Bureau of Economic Geology (BEG) at the University of Texas at Austin conducts research on the status and the trends of coastal habitats as well as shoreline erosion and sea-level rise issues/impacts.

TPWD maintains and operates one of the longest-running coastal monitoring programs in the world (since late 1970s) on coastal living resources, and BEG has one of the strongest and most extensive mapping and coastal characterization programs in the United States. Both of these programs, and the others mentioned above, allow for accurate spatial and temporal tracking of Texas coastal natural resources.

Previous NOAA studies along the upper Texas coast provide a vision of future or predictive scenarios for South Texas coastal species, habitats, and productivity. During the 1980s, extensive studies on salt marshes revealed a glimpse of what might happen to species and secondary productivity when sea-level rise occurs (Zimmerman et al. 1991). Initial or slow flooding of these salt marshes will stimulate growth and abundance of algae, which in turn increases primary consumers and then secondary consumers. Large predatory species may also increase in size and abundance. However, these changes may be transitional or short term, and the benefits can disappear when drowning marshes convert to open-water habitats without plants (Zimmerman et al. 1991).

Subsidence of coastal land and salt marshes in the Houston-Galveston area actually

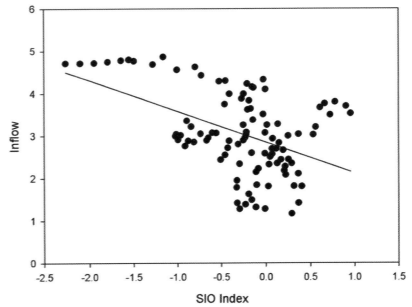

Figure 10. Linear regression relationship between average coast-wide inflow and the SIO index. Same data as plotted in Figure 9.

revealed the above example, but it provides an excellent model of relative sea-level rise impacts on coastal mashes and associated species. Likewise, compilations of data prepared by the Texas BEG and analyzed by the TWDB show the potential changes and relationships between climate and estuaries along the Texas coast (Longley 1995). Under varying climatic scenarios, changes in climate drive changes in freshwater inflow, bay salinity, and sea-level rise. All of these, in turn, impact change or shifts in the distribution and coverage of certain coastal habitats.

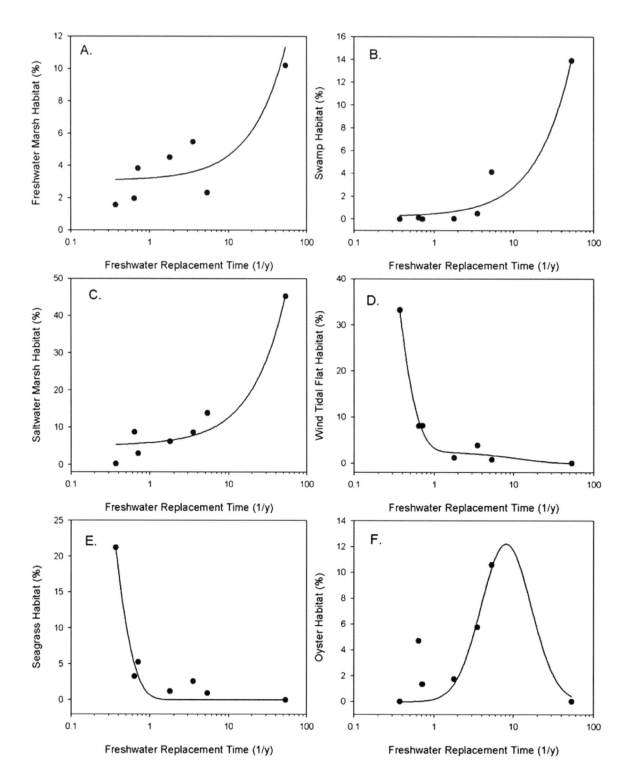

Figure 11. The area of habitat type as percent of total habitat area as a function of different freshwater inflow regimes within each Texas estuary (Table 1, Longley 1995). Freshwater inflow regime is represented as annual freshwater inflow/estuarine volume in units of year. A, B, and C fitted with exponential growth model; D and E fitted with exponential decay model; and F fitted with log normal model (Montagna et al. 2002).

Although, mapping of coastal habitats today is highly accurate with the use of digital aerial photography and Geographic Information Systems (GIS) software, comparisons to older maps and aerial photography less precise. Consequently, trends or directions of habitat change, rather than the actual aerial change or coverage, is more realistic. Longley (1995) gives the current trends in selected coastal habitats within estuaries with increasing freshwater inflow regimes (Figure 11). The inflow regime is represented as the freshwater replacement times per year (1/y), because it is calculated by dividing the freshwater inflow rate (ac-ft/y) by the estuary volume (ac-ft). The replacement rate is analogous to the inverse of the residence time, thus a value of one means that the once per year.

Each point in Figure 11 matches the established percent of habitat coverage within each of the seven estuaries along the Texas coast (Table 1). Long-term inflow changes, and thus habitat change, can occur as a result of increased water use due to human population increases, decreased run-off caused by increased evaporation due to higher temperatures, and increased or decreased run-off depending upon regional changes in precipitation (Longley 1995). Thus, if climate change causes the freshwater inflow regimes to change, then habitat composition within estuaries will change.

As freshwater regime increases, four habitats (freshwater marsh, swamp, saltwater marsh, and oyster reefs) increase by exponential growth models (Figure 11). However, if bays become too fresh because of very high inflow rates (as in Sabine Lake), then oyster populations plummet. The concept that there is an optimal flow and salinity range and maximum carrying capacity for bottom-dwelling organisms, such as oysters, has been shown to be true in the Nueces Delta where data fit a three-parameter log-normal model well (Montagna et al. 2002). Increasing freshwater is bad for some organisms. Seagrass and wind tidal flats decrease exponentially with increasing freshwater inflow regime (Figure 11).

Coupled with freshwater inflow increases or decreases affecting habitat change, sea-level rise is the other substantial driver. Estimates of sea-level rise vary greatly, making credible estimates of changes in habitats difficult. However, trends or direction of change can be predicted with some certainty and resultant consequences can be instructive for natural resource managers. Rising sea-level will cause more frequent and longer inundation of fresh marsh, swamp, and salt-brackish marshes. As fresh marshes and swamps are flooded by saline waters they will be converted to salt-brackish marshes, and eventually open water.

From the Coastal Bend throughout the Laguna Madre, wind-tidal flats could spread inland in low-lying areas. Former wind-tidal flats will convert to seagrass beds in many areas (e.g. land-cut, backside of South Padre Island) as the sea transgresses over this habitat. Seagrass beds will increase in shallow areas where they take over former wind-tidal flats, but they will be lost in deeper water (greater than 1 m) where sufficient light cannot penetrate.

Also, sea-level rise will increase the overall volume of the bays and lagoons, thereby decreasing the ability of freshwater inflows to maintain current salinity regimes (Longley 1995). The higher salinities found in South Texas bays and lagoons (Corpus Christi and Laguna Madre) would "migrate" up the Texas coast/in this scenario.

One critical element in the continued inundation of the coast would be when the sea-level "hits" the minor and major bluffs along shorelines. In addition to the erosion of the mainland, increasing water depth at this steep increase in shoreline elevation would cause termination of the shallow waters necessary for certain habitats (salt marshes, mangroves, wind-tidal flats, and seagrass beds).

Using the Texas Coastal Bend as an example of habitat trends over the past fifty years, we can see increases in estuarine marshes, mangroves, and seagrasses. Concomitantly, we see decreases in tidal flats and Gulf beach habitat, and palustrine marsh remains about the same (White et al. 2006) (Figure 12 and Table 3). The authors of this work stress that they are more confident in the direction of these trends than absolute magnitude (primarily due to the lack of accuracy in dealing with vintage aerial photos and subsequent maps). Their project, involving status and trends of wetlands and aquatic habitats on barrier islands and adjacent bays, covered the entire Texas coast and separate reports delineate changes by coastal region (White et al. 2002, 2004, and 2006).

Mangroves are a good example of species that are likely to increase their range extension because of increased temperatures. For example, early maps of the distribution of black mangroves (*Avicennia germinans*) indicated there were only 65 acres (02.63 km^2) of mangrove habitat in the Mission-Aransas estuary (NOAA 2006). However, it is likely that there are closer to 15,000 to 21,500 acres (60.70 to 87.01 km^2) of mangroves in just the Mission-Aransas estuary alone. This change has occurred primarily within the last twenty years. At one time, the northern range limit of black mangrove was thought to be the Aransas Bay area. Mangroves are also sensitive to changes in elevation and thus would be greatly affected by sea-level rise and erosion. But other more dramatic changes may be in store. Since the hyperactive hurricane season of 2005, red mangroves (*Rhizophora mangle*) have started to take root in several sites along the Texas coast ranging from South Padre Island to Matagorda Island. These are still living as of this writing, and could become well established if winter temperatures remain above freezing. In the recent past, red mangroves have been restricted to tropical climates in Mexico and south Florida. The mangroves can be a sentinel species for temperature change effects along the Texas coast.

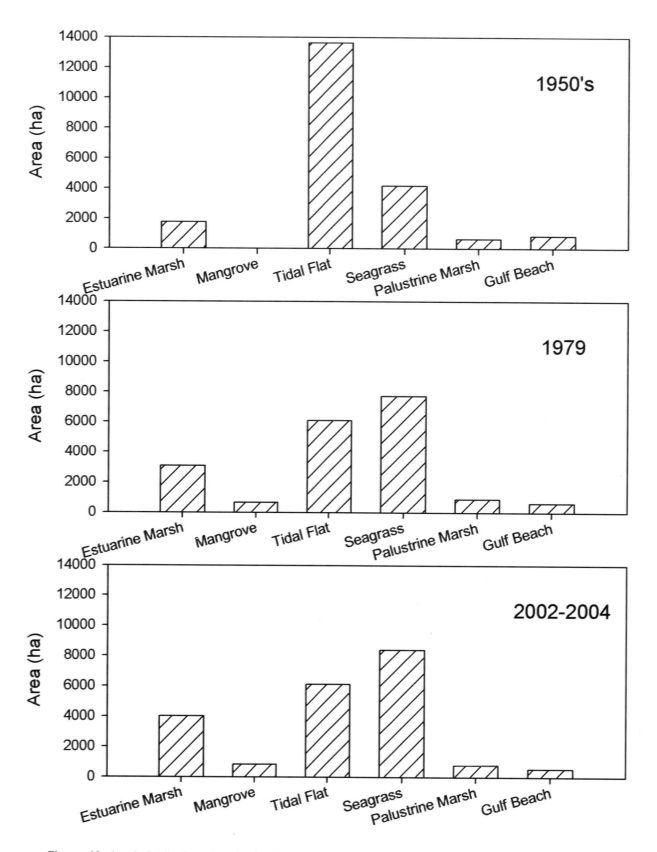

Figure 12. Areal distribution of major habitats in the Texas Coastal Bend in the 1950s, 1979, and 2002-2004 (Table 2, White et al. 2006)

Species ranges are expected to change with changing climate. In some cases these will be extensions of tropical species northward due to increasing temperatures. In other cases, the changes will be related to salinity changes that limit the range of distribution of oligohaline and brackish species.

Table 3. Total area of major habitats in the 1950's, 1979, and 2002-04 in the Texas Coastal Bend (from White et al. 2006)

Habitat	1950s		1979		2002-2004	
	ha	acres	ha	acres	ha	acres
Estuarine Marsh	1,763	4,356	3,087	7,627	4,009	9,906
Mangrove	*	*	665	1,642	837	2,068
Tidal Flat	13,647	33,722	6,114	15,109	6,121	15,125
Seagrass	4,167	10,297	7,704	19,036	8,398	20,752
Palustrine Marsh	665	1,643	890	2,199	767	1,895
Gulf Beach	861	2,128	630	1,557	535	1,322

* = not mapped

Species Changes

Changes in abundance of oligohaline and brackish species are good examples of recent changes that are likely due to increased salinity in Texas estuaries. For example, in Gulf coast estuaries, the clam *Rangia cuneata* has long time been recognized as the dominant benthic animal in areas where salinity ranges from 0 - 15 ppt salinity. In recent studies of Rincon Bayou, in the Nueces Delta Texas, salinities now can be hypersaline, up to 100 ppt and *R. cuneata* is never found alive (Montagna et al. 2002). However, middens of *R. cuneata* were found in the Nueces Delta (Bureau of Reclamation 2000). Middens are piles of shells, which were created by local indigenous people as they feasted on the clams. Most of the clam shells exhibit brakes or marks consistent with those made to open the shell for the meat inside. The middens are composed of clams that are uniform in size 51 cm ± 1.6 cm. (20.08 ± 0.63)Based on published growth rates, these clams are likely five years old. The maximum life span of *Rangia* is fifteen to twenty years. *Rangia* shells this old (about five years) were most likely produced by a large, successfully recruiting population, existing in brackish water conditions for extended periods of time. This is in sharp contrast to current conditions in the Nueces Delta. Two dams were built and the sides of the Nueces River have been diked so fresh water does not spill into the delta. The delta is now hypersaline for extended periods of time and is a reverse estuary. The hypersaline conditions simply result from reduced inflows. The reverse estuary is caused by freshwater entering Nueces Bay below the delta and high tides flooding fresh water into the hypersaline delta. Thus, salinities typically decline toward the lower reaches, not the upper reaches of the delta. The presence of extensive middens indicates the delta benthic community has changed dramatically since dams were built and freshwater inflow has been reduced. The presence of hypersaline and reverse estuary conditions indicate wetland habitats no longer provide historical functions. Thus, if climate change alters inflow patterns such that salinities increase, then it can be expected that similar changes would be common.

Literature Cited

Alvarez, R., M. Sangen, C. Rowan, and L. Moore. 2006. *Fair Warning: Global Warming and the Lone Star State*. Austin Texas: Environmental Defense.

Antoine, J. W., and J. C. Gilmore. 1970. *Geology of the Gulf of Mexico: Ocean Industry.* 34 - 38.

Applebaum, S., P. A. Montagna, and C. Ritter. 2005. Status and Trends of Dissolved Oxygen in Corpus Christi Bay, Texas. *U.S.A. Environmental Monitoring and Assessment* 107:297-311.

Brown, L. F., Jr., J. L. Brewton, T. J. Evans, J. H. McGowen, W. A. White, C. G. Groat, and W. L. Fisher. 1980. Environmental Geologic Atlas of the Texas Coastal Zone – Brownsville – Harlingen Area. *Bureau of Economic Geology* University of Texas at Austin.

Brown, L. F., Jr., J. L. Brewton, J. H. McGowen, T. J. Evans, W. L. Fisher, and C. G. Groat. 1976. Environmental Geologic Atlas of the Texas Coastal Zone – Corpus Christi Area. *Bureau of Economic Geology* University of Texas at Austin.

Brown, L. F., Jr., J. H. McGowen, T. J. Evans, J., C. G. Groat, and W. L. Fisher. 1977. Environmental Geologic Atlas of the Texas Coastal Zone – Kingsville Area. *Bureau of Economic Geology* University of Texas at Austin.

Bruun, P. 1962. Sea-level Rise as a Cause of Shore Erosion. *Journal of the Waterways and Harbors Division* 88:117-130.

Bureau of Reclamation. 2000. *Rincon Bayou Demonstration Project.* Austin, Texas: United States Department of the Interior, Bureau of Reclamation, Oklahoma-Texas Area Office.

Davis Jr., R. A., W. G. Fingleton, G. R. Allen Jr., C. D. Crealese, W. M. Johanns, J. A. O'Sullivan, C. L. Reive, S. J. Scheetz, and G. L. Stranaly. 1973. Corpus Christi Pass: A Hurricane Modified Tidal Inlet on Mustang Island, Texas. *Contributions in Marine Science* 17:123-131.

Diener, R. A. 1975. Cooperative Gulf of Mexico Estuarine Inventory and Study-Texas: Area Description. *NOAA Tech. Report* NMFS Circ. 393, U.S. Department of Commerce.

Douglas, B. C. 1991. Global Sea Level Rise. *Journal of Geophysical Research* 96:6981-6992.

Emanuel, K. 2005. Increasing Destructiveness of Tropical Cyclones over the Past 30[thinsp] Years. *Nature* 436:686-688.

Gibeaut, J. C. and Tremblay, T. A. 2003. *Coastal Hazards Atlas of Texas: A Tool for Hurricane Preparedness and Coastal Management* Austin, Texas: Bureau of Economic Geology, The University of Texas at Austin 3:29.

Gibeaut, J. C., W. A. White, R. C. Smyth, J. R. Andrews, T. A. Tremblay, R. Gutiérrez, T. L. Hepner, and A. Neuenschwander. 2003. Topographic Variation of Barrier Island Subenvironments and Associated Habitats. *Coastal Sediments '03: Crossing disciplinary boundaries: Proceedings, Fifth International Symposium on Coastal Engineering and Science of Coastal Sediment Processes.* Volume CD-ROM: Clearwater Beach, Florida p.10.

Intergovernmental Panel on Climate Change. 2007. *Climate Change 2007: The Physical Science Basis, Summary for Policy Makers* Paris p. 21.

Justic, D., N. N. Rabalais, and R. E. Turner 1996. Effects of Climate Changes on Hypoxia in Coastal Waters: A Doubled CO_2 Scenario for the Northern Gulf of Mexico. *Limnology and Oceanography* 41(5):992-1003.

Larkin, T. J. and G. W. Bomar. 1983. *Climatic Atlas of Texas.* Austin, Texas: Texas Department of Water Resources.

Longley, W. L. 1994. Freshwater Inflows to Texas Bays and Estuaries: Ecological Relationships and Methods for Determination of Needs. *Joint Estuarine Research Study* Texas Water Development Board and Texas Parks and Wildlife Department.

Longley, W. L. 1995. Estuaries. *The Impact of Global Warming on Texas: A Report to the Task Force on Climate Change in Texas* G. R. North, J. Schmandt, and J. Clarkson eds. Austin, Texas: The University of Texas Press p. 88-118.

Kalke, R. and P. A. Montagna. 1991. The Effect on Freshwater Inflow on Macrobenthos in the Lavaca River Delta and Upper Lavaca Bay, Texas. *Contributions in Marine Science* 32:49-77.

McEachron, L. W. and B. Fuls. 1996. Trends in Relative Abundance and Size of Selected Finfishes and Shellfishes along the Texas Coast. *Coastal Fisheries Division, Management Data Series* Austin, Texas.

McGowen, J. H., C. V. Procter, Jr., L. F. Brown, Jr., T. J. Evans, W. L. Fisher, and C. G. Groat. 1976. *Environmental Geologic Atlas of the Texas Coastal Zone – Port Lavaca Area* University of Texas at Austin: Bureau of Economic Geology.

Meckel, T. A., U. S. T. Brink, and S. J. Williams. 2006. Current Subsidence Rates due to Compaction of Holocene Sediments in Southern Louisiana. *Geophyical Research Letters* 33:1-5.

Miller, L., and B. C. Douglas. 2004. Mass and Volume Contributions to Twentieth-century Global Sea Level Rise. *Nature* 428:406-409.

Montagna, P. A. and R. D. Kalke. 1992. The Effect of Freshwater Inflow on Meiofaunal and Macrofaunal Populations in the Guadalupe and Nueces Estuaries. *Texas Estuaries* 15:266-285.

Montagna, P. A. and R. D. Kalke. 1995. Ecology of Infaunal Mollusca in South Texas Estuaries. *American Malacological Bulletin* 11(2):163-175.

Montagna, P. A., R. D. Kalke, and C. Ritter. 2002. Effect of Restored Freshwater Inflow on Macrofauna and Meiofauna in Upper Rincon Bayou, Texas, *USA Estuaries* 25:1436-1447.

Morton, R., J. Bernier, and J. Barras 2006. Evidence of Regional Subsidence and Associated Interior Wetland Loss Induced by Hydrocarbon Production Gulf Coast Region, USA. *Environmental Geology* 50:261-274.

Morton, R. A. and J. G. Paine. 1984. *Historical Shoreline Changes in Corpus Christi, Oso, and Nueces Bays, Texas Gulf Coast.* Austin, Texas: Bureau of Economic Geology, University of Texas at Austin.

Ning, Z. H., R. E. Turner, T. Doyle, and K. K. Abdollahi. 2003. Integrated Assessment of the Climate Change Impacts on the Gulf Coast Region. *Findings of the Gulf Coast Regional Assessment* Baton Rouge, Louisiana: GCRCC and LSU Graphic Services.

Ning, Z. H., R. E. Turner, T. Doyle, and K. K. Abdollahi. 2003. *Preparing for a Changing Climate: Potential Consequences of Climate Variability and Change – Gulf Coast Region* Baton Rouge, Louisiana: GCRCC and LSU Graphic Services.

National Oceanic and Atmospheric Administration. 2006. Final Programmatic Environmental Impact Statement Federal Approval of The Texas National Estuarine Research Reserve And Management Plan. *The Mission-Aransas Estuary* Silver Spring, Maryland: National Ocean Service, Ocean and Coastal Resource Division, Estuarine Reserves Division.

North, G. R., J. Schmandt, and J. Clarkson eds. 1995. The Impact of Global Warming on Texas. *A Report to the Task Force on Climate Change in Texas* Austin, Texas: The University of Texas Press.

Orlando, S. P., Jr., L. P. Rozas, G. H. Ward, and C. J. Klein. 1993. *Salinity Characteristics of Gulf of Mexico Estuaries* Silver Spring, MD: National Oceanic and Atmospheric Administration, Office of Ocean Resources Conservation and Assessment.

Overpeck, J. T., B. L. Otto-Bliesner, G. H. Miller, D. R. Muhs, R. B. Alley, and J. T. Kiehl. 2006. Paleoclimatic Evidence for Future Ice-Sheet Instability and Rapid Sea-Level Rise. *Science* 311:1747-1750.

Paine, J. G. 1993. Subsidence of the Texas coast: Inferences from Historical and late Pleistocene Sea Levels. *Tectonophysics* 222: 445-458.

Paine, J. G., and R. A. Morton. 1993. *Historical Shoreline Changes in Copano, Aransas, and Redfish Bays, Texas Gulf Coast.* Austin, Texas: Bureau of Economic Geology, University of Texas at Austin.

Prouty, J. S., and D. B. Prouty. 1989. Historical Back Barrier Shoreline Changes, Padre Island National Seashore, Texas. *Gulf Coast Association of Geological Societies.* Volume XXXIX: Transactions: 481-490.

Pulich, Jr. W. and C. Blair. 1997. Current Status and Historical Trends of Seagrasses in the Corpus Christi Bay National Estuary Program study area. *CCBNEP* (20) Corpus Christi, Texas.

Ratzlaff, K. W. 1980. Land-surface Subsidence in the Texas Coastal Region. *United States Department of Interior Geological Survey* Austin, Texas p. 19.

Rignot, E., and P. Kanagaratnam. 2006. Changes in the Velocity Structure of the Greenland Ice Sheet. *Science* 31: 986-990.

Robinson, L., P. Campbell, and L. Butler. 2000. Trends in Texas Commercial Fishery Landings, 1972-1998. *Management Data Series No. 173* Austin, Texas: Texas Parks and Wildlife Department.

Sharp, J. M., Jr., S. J. Germiat, and J. G. Paine. 1991. Re-evaluation of the Causes of Subsidence along the Texas Gulf of Mexico Coast and Some Extrapolation of Future Trends. *Fourth International Symposium on Land Subsidence* IAHS 200:397-405.

Shepherd, A., and D. Wingham. 2007. Recent Sea-Level Contributions of the Antarctic and Greenland Ice Sheets. *Science* 315: 1529-1532.

Simms, A. R., J. B. Anderson, and M. Blum. 2006. Barrier-island Aggradation via Inlet Migration: Mustang Island, Texas. *Sedimentary Geology* 187:105-125.

Texas Department of Water Resources. 1982. The Influence of Freshwater Inflows Upon the Major Bays and Estuaries of the Texas Gulf Coast. *Executive Summary* Second Ed. (8) Austin, Texas: Texas Department of Water Resources.

Texas Parks and Wildlife. 1988. *Trends in Texas Commercial Fishery Landings, 1977-1987 Management Data Series* (149) Austin, Texas: Texas Parks and Wildlife Department, Coastal Fisheries Branch.

Tolan, J. M. 2007. El Niño-Southern Oscillation Impacts Translated to the Watershed Scale: Estuarine Salinity Patterns along the Texas Gulf Coast, 1982 to 2004. *Estuarine Coastal and Shelf Science* 72:247-260.

Twilley, R. R., E. J. Barron, H. L. Gholz, M. A. Harwell, R. C. Miller, D. J. Reed, J. B. Rose, E. H. Siemann, R. G. Wetzel, and R. J. Zimmerman. 2001. Confronting Climate Change in the Gulf Coast Region: Prospects for Sustaining our Ecological Heritage. *Union of Concerned Scientists* Washington, DC: Cambridge, Massachusetts, and Ecological Society of America.

White, W. A., R. A. Morton, R. S. Kerr, W. D. Kuenzi, and W. B. Brogden. 1978. Land and Water Resources, Historical Changes, and Dune Criticality: Mustang and North Padre Islands, Texas. *Bureau of Economic Geology* (46) Austin, Texas: The University of Texas at Austin.

White, W. A., T. A. Tremblay, J. Hinson, D. W. Moulton, W. J. Pulich, Jr., E. H. Smith, and K. V. Jenkins. 1998. Current Status and Historical Trends of Selected Estuarine and Coastal Habitats in the Corpus Christi Bay National Estuary Program Study Area. *CCBNEP* (29) Corpus Christi, Texas.

White, W. A., R. A. Morton, and C.W. Holmes 2002. A Comparison of Factors Controlling Sedimentation Rates and Wetland Loss in Fluvial-deltaic Systems, Texas Gulf Coast. *Geomorphology* 44: 47-66.

White, W. A., T. A. Tremblay, R. L. Waldinger, and T. R. Calnan. 2002. *Status and Trends of Wetland and Aquatic Habitats on Texas Barrier Islands, Matagorda Bay to San Antonio Bay* Coastal Coordination Division, Texas General Land Office. Final Report, No. NA07OZ0134.

White, W. A., T. A. Tremblay, R. L. Waldinger, and T. R. Calnan. 2006. *Status and Trends of Wetland and Aquatic Habitats on Texas Barrier Islands Coastal Bend* Coastal Coordination Division, Texas General Land Office. Final Report No. NA04NOS4190058.

Wilkinson, B. H., J. H. McGowen, and C. R. Lewis. 1975. Ingleside Strandplain Sand of Central Texas Coast. *AAPG Bulletin* 59:347-352.

Williams, H. F. L. 1999. Sand-spit Erosion Following Interruption of Longshore Sediment Transport: Shamrock Island, Texas. *Environmental Geology* 37:153-161.

Withers, K. and J. W. Tunnell, Jr. 1998. Identification of Tidal Flat Alterations and Determination of Effects on Biological Productivity of These Habitats Within the Coastal Bend. *CCBNEP* (26) Corpus Christi, Texas.

Zervas, C. 2001. Sea Level Variations of the United States 1854-1999. *NOAA* National Oceanographic and Atmospheric Administration.

Zimmerman, R. J., T. J. Minello, E. F. Klima, and J. M. Nance. 1991. Effects of Accelerated Sea-level Rise on Coastal Secondary Production. *Coastal Wetlands Zone '91 Conference-ASCE.* H. S. Bolton and O. T. Magoon, eds. Long Beach, California, p. 110-124.

4

SOUTH TEXAS CLIMATE 2100:
POTENTIAL ECOLOGICAL AND WILDLIFE IMPACTS

LEONARD A. BRENNAN

In South Texas, the impacts of increased temperature and atmospheric carbon dioxide (CO_2) on the ecological relationships that provide the foundations for wildlife habitats and populations are potentially huge, but largely unknown at present. This is because little research attention has been paid to this issue, which is unfortunate because wildlife are culturally and economically important in this ecological region of a state were wildlife has an annual economic value conservatively estimated at about four billion dollars. Field experiments conducted outside of Texas provide equivocal results with respect to how people think grassland and perhaps shrubland vegetation will respond to increased temperatures and CO_2. If drying trends accompany increases in heat, then many species of amphibians will clearly be at risk. With respect to reptiles, it is unknown, but postulated that rising heat could limit daily activities of lizards, and increase the growth rates of some turtles. Some reptile sex ratios may be influenced by increased heat, because gender is determined by the temperature at which eggs are incubated in some species. Mammalian species in Big Bend National Park are predicted to experience at least a 25% turnover because of a vegetation shift from arid shrub lands to C4 grasslands. If drying trends and extended periods of drought persist, then the annual productivity of two commercially important game species, northern bobwhite (*Colinus virginianus*) and white-tailed deer (*Odocoileus virginianus*) will most likely be reduced. With birds, short-distance migrants are predicted to be more responsive, and hence adaptable to climate change than long-distance migrants. Because they presently exist on the knife-edge of their physiological tolerance, northern bobwhites may experience severe and widespread population declines in South Texas if a 4°C (7.2 °F) increase in average temperature is realized. Whether bobwhites could mitigate this potential problem by shifting their geographic range northward is unknown. The secondary effects of global warming, such as increased or prolonged drought and more intense hurricanes, represent a challenge when it comes to predicting the effects of such events on wildlife. While some wildlife species such as white-tailed deer have the mobility to avoid catastrophic weather events, others do not. Even within-species responses may vary, as indicated by bobwhite response to a recent hurricane in South Texas where adults survived at high numbers but most pre-flight juveniles perished. Even with the potential problems that may be faced by bobwhites and white-tailed deer, wildlife populations in South Texas do not seem as likely to be impacted to the extent of wildlife populations in Boreal and Arctic environments. Nevertheless, there is a significant amount of research opportunity with respect to modeling, predicting, and assessing how impending climate change will influence the distribution and abundance of wildlife in South Texas.

Introduction

"Just because scientists know little or nothing about a particular topic, it does not stop them from writing volumes and volumes about it" —Erwin Goldstein

The above quotation by my tenth grade high school biology teacher was made sometime during in the 1972-1973 school year. The intellectual honesty of Mr. Goldstein still resonates with me after more than three decades. It is an especially apt perspective to set the direction and tone of this chapter on the potential effects of global climate change on the ecological relationships that are the foundations of the habitats and populations of wild vertebrates in South Texas. We actually know very little about what will happen to wildlife in South Texas if the climate continues to warm; therefore we, as scientists, need to train a keen eye and a skeptical perspective on these very first approximations that are emerging in the scientific literature. As much as we would like to think otherwise, the peer-reviewed scientific literature does not hold a monopoly on the truth.

There is no doubt that we are experiencing a long-term climatic warming trend on a global scale (IPCC 2007). The scientific literature is replete with scores of articles on increasing temperature profiles, accumulating greenhouse gasses, melting glaciers, and so on (Inkley et al. 2004). At the present time, such phenomena seem to be irrefutable, and as such will not be discussed in detail here. However, where things get murky is with respect to the predictions of what will actually happen to ecological relationships and wildlife populations in places like South Texas. As we shall see, this is because the projections and predictions in the scientific literature are often equivocal, confusing, and often contradictory when it comes to what we can expect to happen to wildlife populations during the next warming century in South Texas.

There are relatively few published scientific articles on the potential effects of global warming on wildlife in South Texas. Therefore, in this essay, I have drawn from the broader body of scientific literature to deduce how ecological relationships and wildlife populations might change in relation to an ensuing century of increased temperature of about 4°C (7.2 °F). I will begin by using what is presently known about prairie vegetation response to increased CO_2 levels, and then draw from additional published studies to examine what we might expect will happen to selected insect, amphibian, reptile, mammal, and bird populations. Additionally, I will summarize a brief case history using the northern bobwhite (*Colinus virginianus*) as an example of how global warming might influence populations of one of the most economically significant wildlife resources in South Texas. I will conclude with some speculation about what might happen to wildlife populations in light of the predicted secondary effects of global warming such as prolonged periods of drought, and more intense and frequent hurricanes.

Grassland Vegetation

Vegetation is the backbone of most habitats used by terrestrial wildlife. Therefore, it is useful to examine how vegetation might respond to global warming and, by extension, influence wildlife habitat. Whither vegetation, whither wildlife.

South Texas is largely dominated by grassland and grass-shrub vegetation. It is the southern terminus of the North American Great Plains biome. Because scores of bird and mammal species in South Texas rely on prairie grassland and shrubland for their habitat, consideration of how this vegetation might—or might not—respond to climate change is a fundamental aspect of this chapter.

In a recent five-year field experiment, Dukes et al. (2005) exposed plots of California grassland to increased levels of CO_2, temperature, precipitation, and nitrogen deposition. They found that root and shoot production did not respond to elevated CO_2 or warming, an unexpected result. Predictably, adding nitrogen increased total productivity by 26%, mostly by stimulating shoot growth. They concluded that increased rainfall, warming, and CO_2 had little effect on the net primary productivity of the grasslands that they studied.

Results of the study by Dukes et al. (2005) were in contrast to another field experiment where scientists observed an average of 14% increase in biomass production in response to doubled atmospheric CO_2 (Mooney et al. 1999). Also, in contrast to Dukes et al. (2005), Korner (2000) and Morgan et al. (2004) observed that some grasslands responded more positively to elevated CO_2 during dry years, and hypothesized that this might be the case because stomatal openings are narrowed under such conditions and this leads to increased water economy and savings.

Based on the experimental manipulations described above, along with a lack of similar investigations on shrubland vegetation, it is difficult to predict how grassland and shrubland vegetation in South Texas will respond to elevated temperature and CO_2 levels. Replication of the kinds of studies conducted by Mooney et al. (1999), Korner (2000), Morgan et al. (2004), and Dukes et al. (2005) in South Texas grasslands and shrublands would be extremely useful, to say the least.

Insects and Arthropods

Many terrestrial species of insects and arthropods are directly linked to various species of plants. Thus, if the floristic composition of plant communities changes, it is also highly likely that the composition of insect and arthropod communities will also change. Whether the ongoing warming and drying trends will have any impact on the outbreak of pest species is unknown, but it is of particular interest with respect to the cactus moth *Cactoblastus cactorum*. *Cactoblastus* is native to the lower continent of South America, and was discovered in Florida in 1989. It moved northward to South Carolina and westward to the western Florida panhandle during the next six or so years (Zimmerman et al. 2004). This moth is devastating. It is capable of inflicting 100% mortality to species of prickly pear cactus (*Opuntia* spp.) which provide important food resources to many species of wildlife in South Texas and are a major economic commodity in adjacent Mexico.

The actual modes of expansion of *Cactoblastus* are unknown but thought to be anthropogenic. There is a potential implication with warming climate trends and because adults do not lay eggs where temperatures are below 12°C (53.6°F), thus limiting fecundity during winter. If *Cactoblastus* were to become established in South Texas, the incumbent changes in vegetation would be profound, and the effects would be devastating to the many species of wildlife that rely on prickly pear for food and cover.

Amphibians

Populations of amphibians have been declining on nearly a global scale for the past several decades. The causes of these declines are linked to what Collins and Storfer (2003) call Class I and Class II hypotheses. The Class I hypotheses are factors such as exotic species, exploitation, and land use changes. They have been pretty well understood for at least the past century. The Class II hypotheses are much more recent in origin and are related to factors such as changes in climate: ultraviolet radiation, contaminants, and emerging infectious diseases; all of which we have a relatively poor understanding.

Actual predictions of how climate change may impact amphibians in South Texas in light of the Class I and II hypotheses identified by Collins and Storfer (2003) are not clear. This is because it is not clear whether the predicted warming trend will be accompanied by extended periods of drought, or whether current rainfall patterns will remain more or less constant. If drying trends accompany increased ambient temperatures, then obviously this will have a widespread negative effect on nearly all amphibian species because of their close link to wetland habitats. If warming trends are accompanied with adequate rainfall, then species of amphibians will obviously be less severely impacted. In any case, the combination of various Class II hypotheses presents a series of factors that will likely continue to cause widespread declines in amphibians on a global scale, and, by logical extension, in South Texas.

Reptiles

Gibbons et al. (2000) noted that the same series of factors that are apparently responsible for amphibian declines[*] are also linked to declines in reptile populations on a global scale. Inkley et al. (2004) noted that while such predictions are highly speculative, some people have postulated that increases in heat could limit the daily activities of lizards, and increase the growth rates of some turtles.

Like amphibians, geographic ranges of many reptile species are correlated with temperature, so as temperatures change, so too will the distributions of many reptile species. In a number of reptile species such as American alligators (*Alligator mississippiensis*), which are present in coastal areas of South Texas, incubation temperature of eggs can determine the gender of the offspring. Incubation temperatures greater than 34°C (93.2 °F) produce almost all males, whereas females are produced at incubation temperatures less than 30°C (86°F). (Ferguson and Joanen 1982; Joanen and McNease 1989). Whether increases in global temperatures will skew sex ratios of alligators in favor of males is unknown, but perhaps likely.

---

[*] habitat loss, invasive species, contaminants, diseases, unsustainable development, and global climate change

Mammals

While there has been no attempt to assess the role of climate change on the mammals of South Texas, the recent study by Burns et al. (2003) may have implications for this part of the state. Unlike the field experiments that can be used to assess impacts of global warming on vegetation, virtually all assessments of wild vertebrate populations have been conducted using simulation analyses of vegetation changes, which are then correlated to possible shifts in distribution of vertebrate species.

Results from the study by Burns et al. (2003) noted that a doubling of CO_2 levels in Big Bend National Park would result in a loss of ten mammal species (-21% of forty-eight species currently present), and a potential gain of twenty-two new species (+45% of forty-eight species present) for a net turnover of twelve species. This was the greatest level of turnover for any of the eight national parks used in their analysis.

Burns et al. (2003) hypothesized that the Subtropical Arid Shrubland vegetation that presently dominates Big Bend National Park is likely to become a C4 grassland with perhaps a significant proportion of exotic species. "C4" grasses have a unique ability to make compounds from photosynthesis that have four atoms of carbon instead of three, which is the case with most other plants. By taking in an extra atom of carbon during each cycle of photosynthesis, C4 plants are able to limit their loss of water and are hence more drought tolerant than C3 plants.

Although the potential changes in South Texas grassland and shrubland vegetation are likely to be different because of factors such as elevation, the type of scenario predicted by Burns et al. (2003) for Big Bend may have implications for South Texas. This is because much of the South Texas landscape is presently dominated by semi-arid subtropical and shrub vegetation. If a warming and drying trend continues to develop in South Texas, and the scenario predicted by Burns et al. is correct, then the proportions of grassland to shrubland in South Texas may change with a concomitant effect on terrestrial mammals.

Under the scenario of transition from arid shrublands to C4 grasses, Big Bend National Park is predicted to gain four species of bats, four species of carnivores, four species of shrews, two species of rabbits and eight species of rodents. Whether similar changes might be observed in South Texas needs to be investigated. Nevertheless, such changes in species of small mammals could have profound impacts on the higher trophic level carnivores that prey on them.

In an earlier study, Scheel et al. (1996) hypothesized that climate change and global warming would result in an expansion of tropical forests into Texas, and that tree-roosting, but not cavity roosting, bats would be affected by such a change in vegetation. Such contrasting results are indicative of the wide range of predictions generated by simulation analyses of climate change on wildlife.

The potential effects of global warming on white-tailed deer (*Odocoileus virginianus*) populations in South Texas are not clear, although the negative consequences of drought are fairly well-known for large mammals (Ginnett and Young 2000; Lawrence et al 2004; Brown et al. 2006). The warming and drying trend, and resultant reduction in arid land shrubs predicted for Big Bend National Park by Burns et al. (2003) may be a negative factor for white-tailed deer that rely on brushy vegetation. Although highly speculative, a long-term trend towards C4 grasslands may provide an opportunity for pronghorn (*Antilocapra americana*) to recolonize former range in South Texas that became unsuitable from brush encroachment. More likely than the pronghorn scenario described above, a warming and drying trend may also allow desert mule deer (*Odocoileus hemionus)* from West Texas to expand their geographic range east and south. Additionally, white-tailed deer are extensively fed both carbohydrate and protein foods by people throughout South Texas. Whether such extensive feeding programs may mitigate the potentially negative effects of global warming on deer populations is not presently known.

Birds

Except for northern bobwhites[†] there have been, to my knowledge, few efforts to understand the potential impacts of global warming on birds in South Texas. However, there is a growing literature that is documenting fairly dramatic changes in the timing and arrival of breeding migratory birds throughout North America and elsewhere (see for example Dunn and Winkler 1999; Butler 2003; Robinson et al. 2005).

As a point especially germane to South Texas, Butler (2003) hypothesized that short-distance migratory birds (i.e., those wintering in the southern U.S.) may be able to more rapidly adapt to climate change than long-distance migrants (those

---

[†] see section on bobwhite case history below

birds wintering south of the U.S.). This is because short-distance migrants, which now arrive on breeding grounds an average of thirteen days earlier than fifty years ago, can respond to meteorological cues. In contrast, long-distance migrants, which now arrive on breeding grounds an average of four days earlier than fifty years ago, must respond to photoperiod to trigger the timing of their northward journeys to the breeding grounds.

In a simulation analysis, Schwartz et al. (2006) used data on 142 tree and 116 bird species to develop predictions of extinction risk under a scenario of doubled atmospheric CO_2. They found that both birds and tree species with limited geographic distributions were more likely to experience local and regional extinction as compared to species with broad distributions. In general, this has huge implications for endemic species which may be at a high likelihood of extinction, thus making conservation efforts futile.

Northern Bobwhite Case History

The northern bobwhite is one of the most economically significant wildlife resources in South Texas, second only to white-tailed deer. Because of this cultural importance, bobwhites have been the object of a huge amount of research attention (Brennan 1999; Brennan 2007), including a key paper that assesses the potential impact of global warming on their populations in Texas (Guthery et al. 2000).

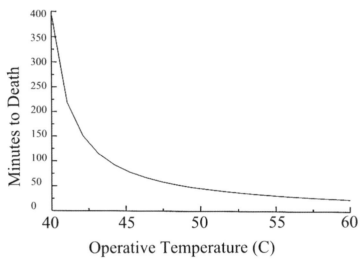

Bobwhites have declined up to 90% throughout the southeastern U.S. (Brennan 1991), and to similar extents in parts of Texas such as the Piney Woods (Whiting 2007), perhaps largely as a function of habitat loss. South Texas remains one of the last bastions of relatively abundant bobwhite populations, although there is emerging evidence that some populations may be declining in this ecological region as well (Hernandez et al. 2007). As an alternative to the habitat-loss hypothesis as a mechanism behind population declines in Texas, Guthery et al. (2000) raised the possibility that global warming could also potentially be responsible for these trends.

Figure 1. Approximate time to death form hyperthermia (core body temperature = 46.5°C) as a function of operative temperature for northern bobwhites. The function is based on a 180 gram bobwhite. (Guthery et al. 2000)

It has been known for decades that bobwhite populations in South Texas fluctuate rather wildly in relation to precipitation (Lehmann 1984). With this conceptual foundation, Guthery et al. (2000) refined the relationship by identifying the role of heat in the context of operative temperatures, or the conditions that bobwhites must cope with on the ground.

Using environmental chamber experiments, Guthery et al. (2000) found that at operative temperatures between 45 and 50°C (113 to 122°F), bobwhite could not survive for much more than an hour (Figure 1). Field data that measured operative temperatures in bobwhite habitat indicated that such operative temperatures were frequently exceeded as much as six or more hours per day (Figure 2), indicating that vast areas of habitat not only became unusable but lethal as well.

In addition to the potential lethality of excess heat, commercial poultry operations have long known that high air temperatures negatively affect food consumption, egg production, eggshell quality, and egg quality of laying chickens. High air temperatures have similar effects on bobwhites (Case and Robel 1974). Thus, the optimum temperature for bobwhites to lay eggs in the field is about 20°C (68°F), and the body mass of females declines for temperatures greater than this threshold. With this as a background, Guthery et al. (1988) estimated that in hot years, average bobwhite hens are in a condition to lay eggs for about sixty days, as opposed to about eighty days in cooler years. When this stressed physiological situation during hot breeding season is coupled with a dramatically reduced proportion (approximately 60% of the hens nesting hens as opposed to 100% nesting which typically occurs during a cooler year), annual productivity can be reduced by up to 1.09 juveniles per adult (Guthery et al. 2000) with potentially disastrous effects on annual productivity.

Up to this point, the role of heat and bobwhite nesting has been considered from the local scale. By disrupting breeding and habitat use on a local scale, global warming could potentially contribute to quail population declines on a continental scale. Whether quail might be able to respond to earlier, warmer spring weather, and initiate breeding one or two months earlier in response to such warming trends remains unknown.

Although almost entirely overlooked by most quail researchers, global warming has been hypothesized to be partially responsible for long-term quail declines (Guthery et al. 2000), especially if warming trends increase by 4 to 5°C (7.2 to 11.8°F) over the next several decades. While habitat loss and fragmentation are most frequently invoked as being the cause of quail population declines, some have noted (Guthery et al. 2000) that there are other places where declines have occurred where there is no apparent loss of habitat. At least theoretically, long-term warming trends could be responsible for quail population declines.

Secondary Effects of Climate Change on Wildlife

Along with an increase in atmospheric CO_2 and average ambient temperature, one of the predictions by climate change experts is a dramatic increase in frequency of secondary effects such as an increase in summer heat waves (successive days greater than 35°C [95°F]), more severe rainstorms (Gong and Wang 2000), prolonged droughts, and more intense hurricanes (IPCC 2007). In this section, I synthesize some of the speculative aspects of how these secondary factors might influence populations of two very economically important game species in South Texas: northern bobwhites and white-tailed deer. These species are used as examples not just because of their economic prominence but also because wildlife scientists actually have some data and experience with respect to how these species respond to such factors.

The effects of severe rainstorms on bobwhites and white-tailed deer are probably minimal, at least under conditions that do not result in severe flooding. Timing of seasonal rainfall can influence breeding phenology of bobwhites. This species usually exhibits peak nesting activity in May and June, typically in relation to a more-or-less regular pulse in spring rain in South Texas. During three to four of the last five years, however, the peak spring rainfall in South Texas has either been absent or delayed until late June or early July. The resulting impact on quail is a delayed breeding season and a low percentage of fully-grown birds at the beginning of hunting season in late October. Many quail managers have been approaching this problem from a stewardship perspective by delaying their quail hunting until late December or early January when the birds are fully grown.

The changes in seasonal timing of rainfall (i.e., shifting of peak annual precipitation from spring to summer as noted above) and increased preponderance of drought both could affect deer and quail negatively, but in somewhat different ways. This is because the life history characteristics of these two species are markedly different. Deer are known as a *k*-selected species because they are a long-lived animal with the potential for populations to approach, and in some cases exceed, the carrying capacity of their environment over many years. On the other hand, quail are known as *r*-selected animals whose populations respond quickly and positively when aspects of the environment become favorable for a rate of rapid population increase.

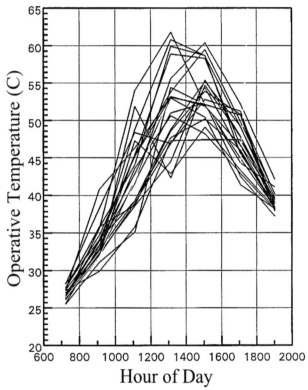

Figure 2. Hourly trends in operative temperature at ground level at twenty-three points in a thicket composed of honey mesquite, Webb County, Texas, June 11, 1996. Drought conditions prevailed when these data were collected. (Guthery et al. 2000)

With deer, a long gestation period usually precludes a rapid (within a year) population response to favorable precipitation and vegetation conditions. On the other hand, quail use something of a bet-hedging strategy and simply delay breeding until the summer rains begin. However, with both deer and quail, the length and frequency of dry periods (in number of years) can be critically important for long-term aspects of age structure and population persistence. Deer have a greater ability than quail to potentially cope with a series of drought years because they simply live longer. However, once conditions again become favorable, quail can respond much more quickly than deer and regain former high levels of population abundance.

Hurricanes probably have minimal negative impacts on deer, but this is not conclusively known. In fact, the increased rainfall may be beneficial for important forb and browse plants. It may also mitigate the potentially negative effects of drought that influence annual fawn productivity and survival, and the habitat use of deer in general (Ginnett and Young 2000; Bello et al. 2004; Lawrence et al. 2004; Gee 2007). However, if an exceptionally fierce hurricane hits at the peak fawning period, annual production could be reduced.

With respect to quail, an important observational study by Hernandez et al. (2002) documented that a hurricane can inflict severe losses on juvenile bobwhites that have not reached flight stage. Apparently, an inability to fly dooms many young birds from rising water whereas adults and more fully-developed juveniles can escape flood waters by roosting in woody vegetation. The average bobwhite brood size of eleven birds (pre-hurricane) was reduced to four (post hurricane) a decrease of 64%.

Mitigation Through Management?

It is both natural and important to pose the question of whether management actions might mitigate the potential negative impacts of secondary effects of global warming on economically important species such as deer and quail in Texas. In the cases of these two very different animals, the common theme revolves around habitat.

With deer, maintaining native brush is essential for providing food and cover needed to meet life history and annual cycle requirements. Management and land-use actions that result in complete brush removal will most likely exacerbate the potentially negative effects of global warming on deer populations in South Texas. Deer have a wide tolerance for a range of brush coverage (greater than 20% to less than 80% cover). However, management actions that result in conditions beyond these extremes will most likely be detrimental.

With bobwhites, the potentially deleterious effects of excess heat are mitigated by brushy cover (Guthery et al. 2000). Grazing management for cattle can also provide potential opportunities for stabilizing and increasing bobwhite populations. By managing grazing in ways that maintain nesting and brooding habitat by keeping adequate grass and forb cover available in a matrix of native brush, it may be possible to sustain bobwhite populations in light of the long-term climate changes that we will most likely continue to experience.

Conclusions

A philosophy of intellectual honesty about what people know and do not know was ingrained in me more than three decades ago by my high school biology teacher. This outlook certainly colors my view about global warming and wildlife in South Texas. As such, it is imperative that we conclude that we have relatively little empirical data that can be used to make reliable predictions about the response of ecological relationships and wildlife populations to global warming in South Texas. Additionally, there have been no efforts at simulation analyses or modeling approaches as a basis to either estimate or predict the effects of climate change on wildlife in South Texas. Because of this severe and unfortunate shortcoming, we must look outside South Texas to nearby or similar regions to make a first approximation of what might happen to wildlife in South Texas as our climate warms. Some field experiments indicate that grassland vegetation is relatively unresponsive to the range of climatic conditions that will be present under a 4°C (7.2°F) increase and a doubling of atmospheric CO_2, while others indicate contrasting results. Whether an area of arid shrublands as vast as Big Bend National Park will actually become dominated by C4 grasses is unknown, but it is predicted by simulation modeling scenarios that also predict a net turnover of 25% of mammalian species richness. Whether such a scenario will influence the distribution and abundance of large mammals such as deer and/or pronghorns remains unknown.

It seems intuitive that short-distance migratory birds could be more responsive and adaptive to climate change than long-distance migrants. South Texas provides wintering habitat for several dozen short-distance migrants, so such a trend might easily influence the amount of time these birds spend on their wintering grounds. With respect to northern bobwhites, a 4°C (7.2°F) increase in ambient temperature could easily contribute to an increase in operative temperatures and have deleterious effects on annual productivity. The only option to mitigate such a problem is through habitat management.

The main point about assessing how South Texas wildlife will respond to climate change revolves around whether we can predict how animals will adapt to or evolve with the changing aspects of their environments. The bottom line is that some animals will be able to cope with such new or changing conditions and some will not.

The most comprehensive assessments of the potential effects of global climate change and wildlife in North America have been developed by Root and Schneider (2001) and Inkley et al. (2004). Among other things, they state that

"The effects of climate change on populations and range distributions of wildlife are expected to be species-specific and highly variable, with some effects considered negative and others considered positive" (Inkley et al. 2004). While it is clear that wildlife and their habitats in boreal and arctic environments are clearly threatened in an ominous and pernicious way by global warming, the effects of global climate change on wildlife in the semi-arid, subtropical environments of South Texas are far less clear.

Acknowledgements

This chapter was made possible with support from the Richard M. Kleberg, Jr. Center for Quail Research. I especially appreciate the constructive review comments provided by Drs. D. Hewitt and F. C. Bryant and J. H. Rappole. This is contribution number 07-110 from the Caesar Kleberg Wildlife Research Institute.

LITERATURE CITED

Bello, J., S. Gallina, and M. Equihua. 2004. Movements of the White-tailed Deer and their Relationship with Precipitation in Northern Mexico. *Interciencia* 29:356-361.

Brennan, L. A. 1991. How Can We Reverse the Northern Bobwhite Population Decline? *Wildlife Society Bulletin* 19:544-555.

Brennan, L. A. 1999. Northern Bobwhite (*Colinus virginianus*). *The Birds of North America* Poole, A and Gill, F. eds. Philadelphia: The Birds of North America, Inc. p.1-28.

Brennan, L. A. 2007. *Texas Quails: Ecology and Management* College Station, Texas: Texas A&M University Press.

Brown, D. E., D. Warnecke, and T. McKinney. 2006. Effects of Midsummer Drought on Mortality of Doe Pronghorn (*Antilocapra americana*). *Southwestern Naturalist* 51:220-225.

Burns, C. E., K. M. Johnson, and O. J. Schmitz. 2003. Global Climate Change and Mammalian Species Diversity in U.S. National Parks. *Proceedings of the National Academy of Sciences* 100:11474-11477.

Butler, C. J., 2003. The Disproportionate Effect of Global Warming on the Arrival of Short-distance Migratory Birds in North America. *Ibis* 145:484-495.

Case, R. M., and R. A. Robel. 1974. Bioenergetics of the Bobwhite. *Journal of Wildlife Management* 38:638-652.

Collins, J. P., and A. Storfer. 2003. Global Amphibian Declines: Sorting the Hypotheses. *Diversity and Distributions* 9:89-98.

Dukes, J. S., N. R. Chiarello, E. E. Cleland, L. A. Moore, M. R. Shaw, S. Thayer, T. Tobeck, H. A. Mooney, and C. B. Field. 2005. Responses of Grassland Production to Single and Multiple Global Environmental changes. *Public Library of Science: Biology* 3(10)1829-1837: e319.

Dunn, P. O. and D. W. Winkler 1999. Climate Change has Affected the Breeding Date of Tree Swallows Throughout North America. *Proceedings of the Royal Society B: Biological Sciences* 266:2487-2490.

Ferguson, M. W. J. and T. Joanen. 1982. Temperature of Egg Incubation Determines Sex in *Alligator mississippiensis*. *Nature* 296: 850-853.

Gee, K. 2007. What to Do About Deer and Drought…. *AgExchange Online News*. Ardmore, Oklahoma: Samuel Roberts Noble Foundation http://www.noble.org/WebApps/AgExchange/AssetQueries/ArticleTemplate_160_97255_104905.html.

Ginnett, T. F. and E. L. Young. 2000. Stochastic Recruitment in White-tailed Deer Along an Environmental Gradient. *Journal of Wildlife Management* 64:713-720.

Gibbons, J. W., D. E. Scott, T. J. Ryan, K. A. Buhlamnn, T. D. Tuberville, B. S. Metts, J. L. Greene, et al. 2000. The Global Decline of Reptiles, Déjà vu Amphibians. *BioScience* 50:653-666.

Gong, D. Y. and S. W. Wang. 2000. Severe Summer Rainfall in China Associated with Enhanced Global Warming. *Climate Research* 16:51-59.

Guthery, F. S., N. D. Forrester, K. R. Nolte, W. E. Cohen, and W. P. Kuvlesky, Jr. 2000. Potential Effects of Global Warming on Quail Populations. *National Quail Symposium Proceedings* 4:198-204.

Guthery, F. S., N. E. Koerth, and D. S. Smith. 1988. Reproduction of Northern Bobwhites in Semi-arid Environments. *Journal of Wildlife Management* 52:144-149.

Hernandez, F., R. M. Perez, and F. S. Guthery. 2007. Bobwhites on the South Texas Plains. *Texas Quails: Ecology and Management* L. A. Brennan ed. College Station, Texas: Texas A&M University Press p. 273-298.

Hernandez, F., J. D. Vasquez, F. C. Bryant, A. A. Radomski, and R. Howard. 2002. Effects of Hurricane Brett on Northern Bobwhite Survival in South Texas. *National Quail Symposium Proceedings* 5:87-90.

Inkley, D. B., M. G. Anderson, A. R. Blaustein, V. R. Burkett, B. Felzer, B. Griffith, J. Proce, and T. L. Root. 2004. Global Climate Change and Wildlife in North America. *Wildlife Society Technical Review* 04-2. Bethesda, Maryland: The Wildlife Society.

IPCC: Intergovernmental Panel on Climate Change. 2007. Climate Change 2007: The Physical Science Basis. *Summary for Policy Makers* Geneva, Switzerland: IPCC Secretariat. www.ipcc.ch

Joanen, T. and L. L. McNease. 1989. Ecology and Physiology of Nesting and Early Development of the American Alligator. *American Zoologist* 29:987-998.

Korner, C. 2000. Biosphere Responses to CO_2 Enrichment. *Ecological Applications* 10:1590-1619.

Lawrence, R. K., S. Demarais, R. A. Relyea, S. P. Haskell, W. B. Ballard, and T. L. Clark. 2004. Desert Mule Deer Survival in Southwest Texas. *Journal of Wildlife Management* 68:561-569.

Lehmann, V. L. 1984. *Bobwhites on the Rio Grande Plains of Texas.* College Station, Texas: Texas A&M University Press.

Mooney, H. A., J. Canadell, F. S. Chapin III, J. R. Ehleringer, C. Korner, et al. 1999. Ecosystem Physiology Responses to Global Change. *The Terrestrial Biosphere and Global Change* B. Walker, W. Steffen, J. Canadell, and J. Ingram, eds. Cambridge, UK: Cambridge University Press. p. 141-189.

Morgan, J. A., D. E. Pataki, H. Clark, S. J. Del Grosso, J. M. Grunzweig, et al. 2004. The Role of Water Relations in Grassland and Desert Ecosystem Responses to Rising Atmospheric CO_2. *Oecologia* 140:11-25.

Robinson, R. A., J. A. Learmonth, A. M. Hatson, C. D. Macleod, T. H. Sparks, D. I. Leech, G. J. Pierce, M. M. Rehfisch, and H. Q. P. Crick. 2005. Climate Change and Migratory Species. *British Trust for Ornithology*, Research Report 414, Thetford, Norfolk, UK: BTO.

Root, T. L., and S. H. Schneider. 2001. Climate change: Overview and Implications for Wildlife. *Wildlife Responses to Climate Change: North American Case Studies* S. H. Schneider and T. L .Root eds. Covelo, CA: Island Press. p.1-56.

Schwartz, M. W., L. R. Iverson, A. M. Prasad, S. N. Matthews, and R. J. O'Connor. 2006. Predicting Extinctions as a Result of Climate Change. *Ecology* 87:1611-1615.

Scheel, D., T. L. S. Vincent, and G. N. Cameron. 1996. Global Warming and the Species Richness of Bats in Texas. *Conservation Biology* 10:452-464.

Whiting, Jr., R. M. 2007. Bobwhites in the East Texas Piney Woods. *Texas Quails: Ecology and Management* L. A. Brennan, ed. College Station, Texas: Texas A&M University Press. p. 156-183.

Zimmerman, H., S. Bloem, and H. Klein. 2004. Biology, History, Threat, Surveillance and Control of the Cactus Moth, *Cactoblastus cactorum*. *Joint FAO and IAEA Report* Vienna, Austria

5

Climate Change Impacts on Regional and Urban Air Quality in South Texas

Jhumoor Biswas and Kuruvilla John

Overview

Temperature changes are precursors to climate variability in a region. Climate change is emerging as an important ingredient of air quality and the link between the two issues will have a significant impact on air quality in the future. The recent Intergovernmental Panel on Climate Change (IPCC) report predicts significant temperature increases over the century. This modeling study presents results from a preliminary investigation, undertaken for a high ozone episode of September 16 to 19, 1999 that affected the South Texas region. The study determines the impact of such temperature perturbations on tropospheric ozone concentrations in this region. These temperature perturbations represented the worst case consequences of extreme climate change within the study region. Significantly large changes in peak ozone concentrations were predicted. Temperatures also had an appreciable spatial impact on the number and extent of eight-hour ozone exceedances with an average of 34% increase in area exceeding the National Ambient Air Quality standards for ozone in the study region for successive increase in temperature. In addition, transboundary flux from major industrialized urban areas also played a major role in supplementing the high ozone concentrations during the perturbed temperature scenarios. It is well known that night-time temperatures have increased at almost twice the rate of daytime temperatures in context of climate change due to increased evaporative cooling during the daytime hours. A sensitivity run was conducted which dealt with the relative influence of daytime versus nighttime increases of temperatures on daily peak ozone concentrations. The nighttime perturbations of ambient temperatures resulted in a disproportionate increase of the daily maximum eight-hour averaged ozone concentration.

The Atmosphere

The atmosphere is a thin blanket of gas enveloping the Earth. The clean atmosphere consists of permanent gases such as nitrogen (78%), oxygen (21%), hydrogen, helium, and inert gases such as argon and krypton in minor quantities. The variable gases in the atmosphere include water vapor, carbon dioxide, methane, and ozone. Ozone (O_3) is a gas that occurs in two layers of the atmosphere: the stratosphere and the troposphere. The stratospheric ozone layer extends upward from about ten to thirty miles above the Earth's surface. It protects life on Earth from the Sun's injurious ultraviolet rays (UV-b). Ironically, ozone found in the troposphere, the layer of the atmosphere that extends from the Earth's surface to about ten miles on top of the Earth's surface, is considered to have detrimental effects on human health and ecosystem when it exceeds certain levels. It is also a key ingredient of photochemical smog occurring mostly in the summer months. Amongst other pollutants of the atmosphere: nitrous oxides, volatile organic compounds, carbon monoxide, sulfur dioxide, and coarse and fine particulate matter are regarded to have the greatest impact on human health when the atmosphere contains harmful levels of these contaminants. With the exception of surface ozone and fine particulates, these air pollutants are primary air pollutants since they are directly emitted via processes from the emissions sources such as ash discharged from a volcanic eruption or the carbon monoxide gas released from motor vehicle exhaust. Ground level ozone is secondary in nature produced by non-linear complex interactions between primary precursors including oxides of nitrogen (NO_x) and volatile organic compounds (VOCs). Secondary aerosols are formed from composite gas reactions.

The Earth's atmosphere is regarded as an unremitting compressible fluid. The atmospheric dynamics governed by prevailing equations of turbulence, mixing, transport, motion of synoptic weather phenomena, and large scale wind circulations operate on a variety of spatial scales ranging from micro scales of motion on a few millimeters to a global scale encompassing thousands of kilometers in an Eulerian framework which is considered fixed with respect to space coordinates. The critical atmospheric chemical phenomena such as urban and regional air quality, toxic air pollution, and aerosol climate interactions range from regional mesocale to large-scale macroscale and are greatly influenced by meteorological features on these spatial and temporal scales.

In essence, climate represents the mean behavior of meteorological weather patterns and varies naturally over all temporal and spatial scales. The interaction between air quality and climate is a two-way interactive process. Human-induced anthropogenic emissions affect climate variability and the resultant climate changes impact background global chemistry and background levels of global air pollutant concentrations. Thus, the interactions play an increasingly important role in local and regional air quality background concentrations. The basic driving force in both air quality problems and anthropogenic climate change is the accumulation of air pollutants in the atmosphere through human activities. The effect of global air pollution on climate can occur through global warming produced by accretion of carbon dioxide levels in the atmosphere through increasing fossil fuel combustion and damages to agricultural and natural ecosystems worldwide by rising air pollutant concentrations that have a strong bearing on climate. Aerosols, which are ubiquitous air pollutants, change global climate through their direct and indirect effects on radiative forcing that cause climate cooling, and counter the warming effects of green house gas warming. However, large uncertainties are associated with climate forcing due to radiative energy transfer by aerosols. Regional air quality in the future depends on a variety of factors. In the near future the state of regional air quality is likely to be associated with the pollutant emission changes allied with progression of urban growth (Dentener et al. 2005) and a combination of the growth of in-situ local emissions and changes in distant emissions (Parrish et al. 1993) transported by intercontinental transport which can alter baseline concentrations (Szopa et al. 2006). In the distant future of 2150, climate change due to radiative forcing modifications and global warming may affect meteorological variables such as temperature and water vapor, consecutively impacting tropospheric chemistry and air quality.

The South Texas region is characterized by a unique climatology of semi arid coastal and inland areas. This region shares an extensive border with Mexico and is currently experiencing greater economic and commercial activity primarily on account of the North American Free Trade Agreement (NAFTA) with Mexico. The growing industrialization and rising population in this region will jeopardize air quality and thus effective air quality assessment, planning, and management programs are a necessity. The primary objectives of the air quality management programs are to determine ambient air pollutant concentrations; ascertain emission sources and their relative impact; and develop concerted efforts incorporating cost effective emission control policies to regulate air pollutants at local and regional levels. There has been little focus so far on effect of potential temperature perturbations arising as a consequence of climate change on regional and urban air quality in the South Texas region. From the perspective of planners, emissions control policies are currently implemented assuming that climate is constant. Based on the results from most recent climatic models, the Intergovernmental Panel on Climate Change report (IPCC 2007) predicts an average rise of global temperature between 1.4 to 6°C (2.52 to 10.8°F) by the year 2100. The significance of the role of possible climate variability on the future of air quality in South Texas needs to be investigated so that future potential emission abatement strategies may be developed factoring climate change in the decision making process for this region.

Air Quality Standards

The Clean Air Act (CAA) amendments previously undertaken in 1990 requires United States Environmental Protection Agency (USEPA) to set National Ambient Air Quality Standards (NAAQS) for principal air pollutants also known as 'criteria' pollutants: ozone (O_3), particulate matter (PM), carbon monoxide (CO), sulfur dioxide (SO_2) and lead (Pb) to safeguard public health especially of those "sensitive" populations such as asthmatics, children, and the elderly. The CAA

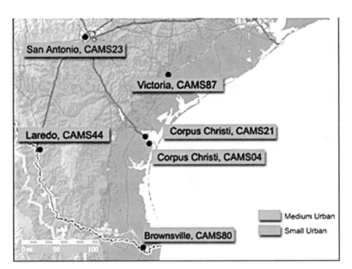

Figure 1. Observational sites in South Texas

lists secondary standards that set limits to protect public welfare, including visibility impairment and property damage. It regulates air toxics also known as hazardous air pollutants (HAPS) and sets specific goals to reduce emissions from all emission sources. The CAA requires intervallic appraisal of the science upon which the standards are based and the standards themselves. Details of the air quality standards and their consequences have been presented in (EPA 2001).

In 1997, EPA revised the existing one-hour ozone standard for ozone to an eight-hour averaged ozone standard which required that the fourth highest eight-hour averaged ozone concentrations in each year averaged over a three-year consecutive period be no greater than 0.08 parts per million (ppm) at any location. In September, 2006, EPA modified the existing twenty-four-hour fine particle standard from 65 micrograms per cubic meter ($\mu g/m^3$) to 35 $\mu g/m^3$. These stringent air quality standards based on health impacts have resulted in widespread non-attainment designation since spatial and time scales are intrinsically related in the air quality processes (Rao 1997; Hogrefe et al. 2006). Recently, USEPA has proposed to further tighten the ozone standard without factoring in any consideration to climatic variability.

Air Quality Status over South Texas

The region of South Texas, which includes the urban and semi urban areas of San Antonio, Corpus Christi, and Victoria, has been visited by several high ozone episodes in the years 1995, 1999, and 2002. These urban areas have been uniquely classified by the Texas Commission on Environmental Quality (TCEQ) to be in near non-attainment status since some of these regions are close to infringing eight-hour ozone standards. Although Corpus Christi has exhibited a decline in the eight-hour averaged ozone concentrations, in recent times San Antonio has exhibited an upward shift in the eight-hour averaged ozone concentrations. Meteorology plays a significant role on ozone exceedances (Seaman and Michelson 2000) and South Texas is no exception to the rule. Ozone episodes in South Texas are characterized by winds from the northeast that transport air pollutants from the industrialized zones of Houston-Galveston into South Texas (Kumar and John 2002). The coastal sea breeze induces the pollutants further inland towards San Antonio.

Major haze events with poor visibility and relatively high levels of $PM_{2.5}$ have been observed over the South Texas region in recent times. Evaluation of long-range transport during haze events identifies major source regions affecting the urban areas of South Texas. Typical haze events have occurred during September and during early spring months of April and May in South Texas cities of San Antonio and Corpus Christi. During the September 2002 haze event, a high-pressure system with prevailing northeasterly winds had stagnated for several days to accumulate the haze over the middle Mississippi River Valley, lower Ohio River Valley, and Tennessee and transported the haze into South Texas. A high-pressure system was also observed during the May 2003 haze event and prevailing southeasterly winds transported particulate matter from Mexico and Central America into South Texas (Kim et al. 2004).

Amongst air toxics, benzene reveals an increase in concentrations in South Texas probably due to proliferation of traffic (Shiohara et al. 2005).

Air Quality Trends in South Texas

A study of air quality trends enhances the understanding of the behavior of air pollutants at urban sites. It is essential for preserving air quality in these regions. It provides greater insight in gauging the effectiveness of past and existing regulatory programs in improving air quality.

Ozone trends are evaluated from observational data collected over a period of several years at observational sites. Each year, federal and state agencies are responsible for gathering and providing quality assured observational data at established monitoring sites around the country. Monitoring stations in South Texas are maintained by TCEQ. The monitoring sites in South Texas have been represented in Figure.1

The ozone trends in South Texas were evaluated utilizing EPA guidelines (EPA 1999) to compute the design values for observed eight-hour ozone concentrations at each monitoring site. The eight-hour ozone design value is equal to the average of the fourth highest annual daily maximum eight-hour values for the most recent three years at that site. The longer-term averaging period provides a methodology for reducing the dependence of the ozone design values on variable short-term meteorological effects (Jones et al. 2005). This is important since changes in ambient ozone concentrations due to changes in meteorological conditions can mask the changes due to changes in ozone precursor emissions, and becomes difficult to assess the impact of the regulatory programs on ozone air quality (Rao et al. 1992).

The eight-hour ozone design values in selected observational sites at coastal and inland regions of South Texas have been represented in Figure 2 and Figure 3 to highlight the variability in trends distinctly by site locations. The long term trends were estimated for the years 1990-2006.

Figure 2 highlights the air quality trend in coastal Corpus Christi. It shows that, despite Corpus Christi having high ozone values in the years 1995, 1999, and 2002, there is a dramatic improvement in eight-hour ozone concentrations with an approximate 31% decrease from 2002 through 2006. San Antonio (Figure 3) conversely exhibits an upward trend in contemporary eight-hour ozone design value for 2003-2005 (86 ppb). It also shows a larger number of ozone exceedances than Corpus Christi over the years for which this analysis was performed. The reasons could be attributed to both natural causes such as direction of air parcel trajectories transporting air pollutants into San Antonio and human-induced relatively greater extent of urban sprawl and commercialization in San Antonio. Brownsville and Laredo are in compliance of eight-hour ozone standards with semi-urban Laredo having eight-hour averaged ozone values below 70 ppb.

In the case of fine particulate matter (PM), the three-year annual average arithmetic mean and the average 98th percentile in San Antonio, Brownsville and Laredo were found to be in compliance with the National Ambient Air Quality Standards for PM by a reasonable margin. The three-year annual average arithmetic mean and annual averaged 98th percentile of twenty-four-hour average $PM_{2.5}$ data in the Corpus Christi region for 2000-2006 were $8.0 \mu g/m^3$ and $22.5 \mu g/m^3$, respectively and this region is also in compliance with the PM NAAQS. However, the trends in fine particulate matter computed for South Texas for the years 2000-2006 for the Corpus Christi area (Figure 4) shows a gradual increase in the $PM_{2.5}$ concentrations. This slow rise in particulate matter concentrations is also duplicated in San Antonio. The spatial correlations between monitoring sites at San Antonio & Corpus Christi were low (less than 0.4) indicating large spatial variability between coastal and inland sites.

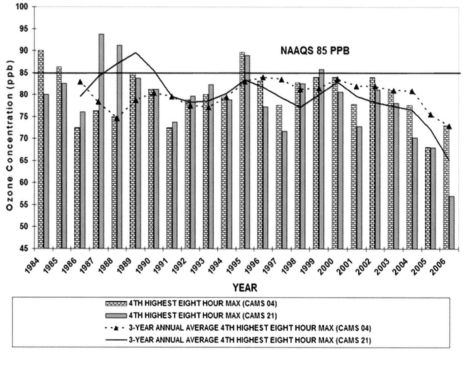

Figure 2. Eight-hour ozone value design trends in Corpus Christi

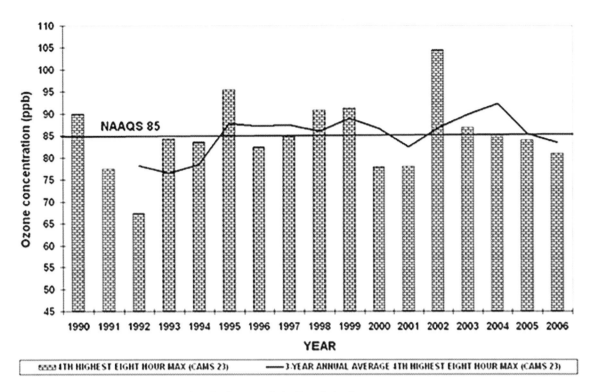

Figure 3. Eight-hour ozone value design trends in San Antonio

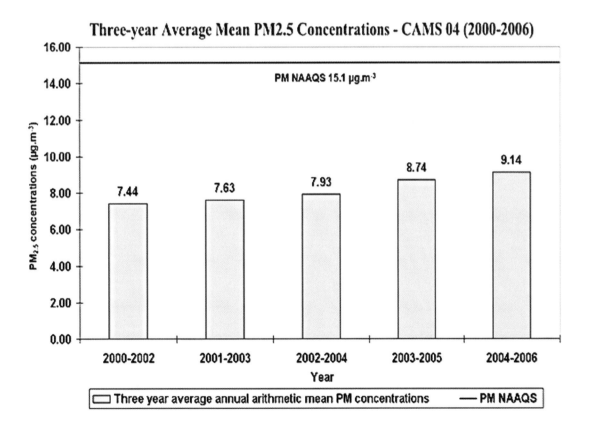

Figure 4. Trend in fine particulate matter concentrations in Corpus Christi

Air Quality Planning Processes

The study of air quality trends in South Texas has reinforced the fact that the urban regions need to design appropriate planning processes to continue to remain in attainment especially of eight-hour national ambient ozone standards. Henceforth, this study will be devoted to ozone quality since maintaining the eight-hour ozone standards currently represents the greatest challenge in air quality in the South Texas Region.

State Implementation Plans (SIPs) are critical components of the air quality planning procedures and consist of emission reduction strategies essential for meeting clean air standards and Clean Air Act requirements conjunctively. In brief, the SIPs include state-issued, USEPA-approved orders requiring pollution restrictions for individual companies and planning documents such as area-specific compilations of emissions estimates and computer simulated modeling analyses. These estimates and analyses demonstrate that the suggested regulatory proposals assure that the air pollutants in the region will meet air quality standards.

Adopted by urban regions in South Texas such as Austin and San Antonio, the EPA's Early Action Compact (EAC) is another type of air quality planning process that permits a region to submit an early State Implementation Plan which delineates steps the region will take to maintain compliance with the eight-hour ozone standards. In return, the EPA will postpone any potential non-attainment designation and give the area until 2007 to demonstrate attainment of the standard. In contrast, the urban area of Corpus Christi has gotten into an agreement with EPA called the O3Flex plan. This plan allows the area to maintain voluntary controls of emissions that will become mandatory only if the area violates the eight hour standard, thus giving the region a headstart on strategic planning for air quality improvement.

EPA supports innovative methods to mitigate emissions reduction potential of unconventional sources. Air pollution control programs in the U.S. have had difficulty regulating the emissions from irregular sources. Emissions from such sources are counteracted by the creation of feasible voluntary air quality programs. The region submitting a SIP first identifies and describes voluntary emission control processes it wishes to incorporate along with estimates of emission reductions attributable to the program. It commits to monitor, evaluate, and report the resulting emissions effects of the voluntary measure; and to remedy in a timely manner any SIP credit shortfall if the voluntary emission reduction program fails to achieve projected emission reductions. The different urban subdomains in South Texas are committed to voluntary reduction measures as part of their State Implementation Plans.

Conceptual Model

Any air quality planning procedures are based on a study of representative high ozone concentrations and development of emission reduction measures for their abatement. Therefore, the ultimate air quality study results should capture the most representative air pollution conditions in the region. Selection of the study period whether episodic, multi episodic, or seasonal is a crucial constituent of the entire effort. According to a study conducted by Durrenberger et al. (1999), identification of days with emission events or unusual conditions correlating with the high ozone concentrations is an important factor in an area with a large number of point sources as is the case with major urban areas in South Texas.

Synoptic meteorological patterns characterized by high pressure, high temperatures, and low winds are conducive to high ozone formation. A conceptual model is a qualitative methodology of characterizing the meteorological conditions that occur during high ozone episodes. A conceptual model was utilized to first identify the high days of ozone concentrations and their characteristic meteorological patterns in the South Texas region from observed data.

There are three layers to a conceptual model.

- Preliminary Conceptual Model (PCM): developed for episode selection for initial eight-hour modeling.
- Interim Conceptual Model (ICM): modifications of the PCM during the development of the modeling protocol and base case study.
- Refined Conceptual Model (RCM): an advanced depiction of evaluation after initial modeling has been completed, control strategies have been implemented, and advanced monitoring has been performed.

The PCM is a series of analyses involving meteorological data, monitored ozone concentrations, and emissions inventory data during periods of high ozone. The additional analysis includes trajectories using trajectory models, data from monitoring, observational modeling, results from previous photochemical modeling, and regional scale modeling. Synoptic weather charts and National Weather Service data can be used to determine the influence of large-scale meteorological conditions, such as hurricanes.

Based on conceptual modeling, elevated ozone concentrations were identified during the month of September for the years 1995, 1999, and 2002 in South Texas region. The eight-hour ozone design values represented earlier confirm these results. The high ozone episode of September 1999 has been used as the archetype of the ozone episodes in the South Texas region and is used in this study.

Air Quality and Climate Change

The issues of air quality and climate are intrinsically interwoven by a number of scientific commonalities. They are both subject to inherent uncertainties related to the complexity of the processes that link emissions to effects and in envisaging the consequences of these processes. The major difference is that emissions responsible for most air-quality related problems have relatively short residence times in the atmosphere. Also, these emissions can be diminished or removed by implementation of air pollution control devices or treatment of emissions. In contrast, several greenhouse gases have much longer residence times of several centuries as in the case of carbon dioxide (CO_2) which is the most important greenhouse gas. Carbon dioxide release is an innate corollary of fossil fuel combustion and sequestering of carbon emissions is a complex and expensive enterprise. The accumulation of CO_2 in the atmosphere leads to the phenomenon of global warming. The other precursor of both air pollution and climate is aerosols which generate a complementary cooling effect due to radiative forcings. Anthropogenic aerosols are produced via primary emissions due to fossil fuel combustion as well as the formation of secondary aerosols by chemical kinematics in the atmosphere. Air quality deterioration and climate change are therefore linked by the human-stimulated energy-generating combustion processes. Policy actions taken to address one of these problems might influence the other. Emissions are also rising globally and the long-range transport of air pollutants and changes in background global chemistry are becoming increasingly important to local, regional, and continental air quality background concentrations that impact regional air quality as well as climate change.

The connection of human activities on a regional scale related to climate change leading to global warming is a well-studied issue and a longstanding topic of concurrent scientific debate (Lindzen 1997). Global climatic models (GCMs) (Friedlingstein et al. 2003; Manabe and Joos et al. 1993; Plattner et al. 2001) have been employed in several studies to predict the climate scenarios of future years (Lenton 2000; Liu and Rodriguez 2005). Only in recent years has there been an emergent awareness of the possible impact of global scale climatic variability on regional air quality. As explained previously, since climate change and air quality are interrelated issues, it becomes important to speculate the consequences of climate change on future air quality in South Texas with the caveat that there is a great deal of uncertainty regarding both these issues.

The principal way climate change can impact air quality is of course by influencing the meteorological parameters, especially temperatures. The influence of meteorology on air pollution dynamics is a well established fact. The strong ozone sensitivity to meteorological conditions, especially to temperature variations, has been amply demonstrated in the past through numerous modeling studies (Sillman and Samson 1995; Chen et al. 2003; Neftel et al. 2002). The Intergovernmental Panel on Climate Change report, (IPCC 2007) based on results from most recent climatic models, predicts an average rise of global temperature between 1.4 to 6°C (2.52 to 10.80°F) by the year 2100. This significant rise of temperature may increase natural levels of background ozone concentrations on the global scale which will increment its relative contribution towards surface ozone concentrations and ozone exceedances on the regional and urban scale. Escalating temperatures can also influence the concentration and distribution of air pollutants through an assortment of direct and indirect processes, such as the alteration of biogenic emissions (Constable et al. 1999); the modifications of chemical reaction rates; the changes in mixed-layer heights that affect vertical mixing of pollutants and therefore regional and urban air quality (Biswas and Rao 2001); and variations of synoptic flow patterns that govern pollutant transport. The impact of aerosol forcings on potential temperature perturbations is beyond the scope of this particular study.

As revealed previously, the South Texas region has experienced exceedances of eight-hour National Ambient Air Quality Standards in different urban and semi urban regions in recent times (University of Texas, Austin, Texas 2004). Extensive emission reduction policies have been developed for this region to continue to remain in attainment of the eight-hour ozone standards in the future. There has been little focus so far on the effect of temperature perturbations as a consequence of climate change on forthcoming regional and urban ozone quality in the South Texas region. Emissions control policies in these parts are currently implemented assuming constancy of climate. This study proceeds to study the possible effects of climate changes on ozone concentrations in the South Texas area. It hopes to enhance the awareness of decision makers regarding the climate change impact on surface ozone concentrations so that future potential emission abatement strategies may be developed that factor climate change in the decision-making process for the South Texas region.

Air Quality Modeling

Air quality models are complex, sophisticated, three-dimensional Eulerian models that, in tandem with three-dimensional meteorological models, can simulate atmospheric dynamics and chemical processes. The Clean Air Act Amendments of 1990 mandated the usage of selected air quality simulation models as the requisite regulatory tools for analyzing the urban and regional problem concerned with high ambient ozone levels across the U.S. (EPA 1991). These models have been typically applied to study representative ozone episodes (Russell and Dennis 2002) and establish ozone abatement strategies as mandated by (EPA 1999) in ozone non-attainment regions. These emission reduction strategies developed with these air quality models have been a vital part of the State Implementation Plans submitted to the EPA by each individual state.

A variety of numerical modeling experiments including employment of process modeling tools (Menut 2003) and chemical transport models (Baertsch-Ritter et al. 2004) have been successfully conducted in the past to study ozone sensitivity to different modifications in temperatures. They conclusively revealed that higher temperatures are usually associated with elevated ozone concentrations. It has also been effectively demonstrated by preceding ozone modeling sensitivity studies that temperature deviations have the largest impact on peak ozone concentrations and ozone exceedances (Dawson et al. 2006) relative to other meteorological variables. This study utilized a photochemical model to assess the impact of perturbed temperatures in the South Texas region. The model simulations were performed with emissions and other meteorological parameters held constant. This type of ozone sensitivity study assists in focusing exclusively on spatial and temporal responses in modeled peak surface ozone concentrations and ozone exceedances to varying temperature perturbations. This study will elucidate effects of global warming on future ozone concentrations and ozone exceedances in South Texas.

Model Description

The Comprehensive Air quality Model with extensions (CAMx), version 3.1 (Environ 2002) was applied in assessing the impact of perturbed temperatures in the South Texas region. The photochemical model CAMx that simulates various atmospheric physical and chemical processes was applied in a nested mode in this study. The base case and the modeled temperature perturbation simulations were performed for the ozone episodic period of September 13 to 21, 1999 that occurred in South Texas. The initial conditions for the modeling system were set at background levels. The photochemical model is in Lambert conformal projection system centered at (-100, 40) with standard parallel latitudes at 30 and 60 degrees respectively. The coarse outermost grid of the photochemical modeling domain grid resolution 36 km (22.37 mi) covers the south, southwest, and central part of continental U.S. The inner grid of 12 km (7.46 mi) grid resolution envelops the Houston-Galveston area, Beaumont-port Arthur area, Dallas Fort Worth area, and the eastern Texas region. The innermost grid of 4 km (2.49 mi) grid resolution containing 90 x 108 cells is focused on South Texas and covers all the (NNAS) of this region (San Antonio, Victoria, and Corpus Christi). The fourteen vertical layers in CAMx extend from the surface up to 4 km (2.49 mi). Further details regarding the model set up have been presented in (Environ 2002).

The Emission Processing System, version 2 (EPS2) (EPA 1992) was utilized to process emission inventory over the modeling domain and generate CAMx ready input gridded emission files. The report (Environ 2002) contains the details concerning the emissions inventory and emissions processing for the ozone episode of September, 1999.

Hourly meteorological data from September 13 to September 21, 1999 were simulated with the Fifth Generation Pennsylvania State University/National Center of Atmospheric Research (PSU/NCAR) Meteorological Model (MM5), version 4.3, (Grell et al. 1993) in a three-way nested grid mode to produce gridded three-dimensional meteorological inputs for the CAMx photochemical model. The meteorological model used analysis grid nudging and the TCOON (Texas Coastal Ocean Observation Network) data for observational based nudging along the coast. The MM5 model consists of twenty-eight half sigma levels in the vertical. Details regarding the meteorological model simulations have been presented in the report (University of Texas, Austin and Environ 2004)

Methodology

The base case modeling simulations for the September ozone episodic period were evaluated using statistical matrices prescribed by EPA (1999) for daily eight-hour average and eight-hour maximum ozone concentrations. A series of additional sensitivity simulations were performed in which the surface and upper air temperatures were perturbed by varying degrees ranging from 1 to 6 °C (1.8 to 10.80°F) in accordance to the anticipated global temperature changes predicted in IPCC (2007) over the entire nested modeling domain maintaining the other meteorological variables constant. This analysis was conducted for high ozone days of September 16 to 19, 1999 after allowing a spin up for three days and only in the surface grid cells of the 4 km (4.29 mi) modeling domain encompassing the South Texas region. The main metrics used for comparison are the spatial variations of differences of eight-hour ozone maxima, the eight-hour ozone exceedances, the number of eight-hour ozone exceedances (greater than 84 ppb) and the number of surface grid cells exceeding the average eight-hour ozone standard in these regions.

Results and Discussions

Base Case Model Evaluation

The base case modeling validation is important to establish confidence in the performance of the model. The model can then be used to develop future emission reduction strategies for the region. In this case, the model evaluation for the base case model run using statistical criteria was undertaken. It was found that all the performance metrics were within the limits set by the EPA performance criteria. Further details of model evaluation and validation can be obtained from (Environ 2002). The model does underpredict ozone concentrations at an observational site in the coastal region of Corpus Christi but, on the days of highest ozone concentrations, it performs relatively well (Figure 5). The model behaves satisfactorily in the inland areas of San Antonio, Brownsville, Laredo, and Victoria. It meets the EPA prescribed performance metrics at these locations. Overall, the model performs relatively well at inland sites in comparison to coastal sites.

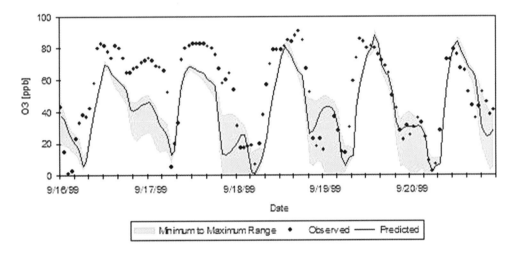

Figure 5. Observed versus model-predicted hourly concentrations at a monitoring site in Corpus Christi

Spatial Impact

The spatial differences in distributions over the entire South Texas region have been summarized in Table 1. It was found for 6°C (10.80°F) perturbation that the greatest increase of about 8.5 ppb from the base case occurred in the southwest San Antonio region, northwest Austin, and the counties bordering Houston-Galveston (Figure 6). Corpus Christi revealed a maximum impact of above 6 ppb. The spatial distribution of the differences in the eight-hour ozone episodic maxima between the base and the perturbed cases remains the same the same for all other perturbed temperature scenarios differing only in the magnitudes. The utmost impact on peak eight-hour ozone concentrations is an almost constant increment of about 1.4 ppb from the preceding temperature perturbed case (Table 1).

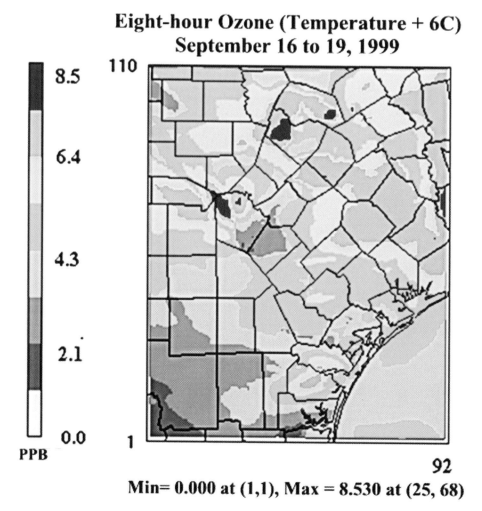

Eight-hour Ozone (Temperature + 6C)
September 16 to 19, 1999

Min= 0.000 at (1,1), Max = 8.530 at (25, 68)

Figure 6. Spatial distribution of the differences in episode maxima of eight-hour ozone concentrations between base case and perturbed temperature case (+6°C [10.80°F])

Table 1. Maximum impact of perturbed temperature

	+2°C	+3°C	+4°C	+5°C	+6°C
Difference in eight-hour ozone concentration in ppb	3.04	4.49	5.88	7.24	8.53

Peak Ozone Impacts

The temperature perturbations have the maximum impact on urban regions. Hereafter, the analysis will be focused in the urban regions of San Antonio, Corpus Christi, and Victoria. The model-predicted eight-hour averaged ozone concentrations were extracted at the compliance grade monitoring sites (CAMS) located at San Antonio, Victoria, and Corpus Christi and maintained by TCEQ. Table 2 illustrates the impact of temperature perturbations on the model-predicted eight-hour episodic peak ozone concentrations averaged over the CAMS sites grouped for each NNA subdomain. The coastal sea breeze blows the ozone further inland, away from Corpus Christi into San Antonio which exhibits the highest episodic eight-hour ozone concentrations amongst all CAMS sites followed by Victoria and Corpus Christi.

Table 2. Episode maximum ozone concentrations (ppb) at South Texas urban sites

	Perturbed Temperatures					
	Base	**+2°C**	**+3°C**	**+4°C**	**+5°C**	**+6°C**
San Antonio	79.80	85.45	86.34	87.19	88.02	88.80
Corpus Christi	71.28	76.11	77.12	78.08	78.99	79.80
Victoria	74.06	78.29	79.18	80.00	80.74	81.42

Ozone Exceedances Impact

Spatial Impact of Eight-hour Ozone Exceedances

Ozone exceedance values (greater than 84 ppb) are important from the standpoint of health and hence from a regulatory perspective. Figure 7 characterizes the spatial pattern of eight-hour ozone exceedances for 3°C (5.40°F) temperature perturbations chosen as a representative case. The maximum impact is again in the San Antonio region (greater than 90 ppb), and in the counties north-east of Victoria close to Houston, which are affected by the transboundary flux from industrialized regions that supplement the ozone concentrations in South Texas. Corpus Christi is less affected compared to the inland urban regions due to the sea breeze influence on air pollutants. In case of the extreme 6°C (10.80°F) perturbed scenario, the eight-hour ozone exceedances become more widespread in San Antonio than any other urban region in South Texas.

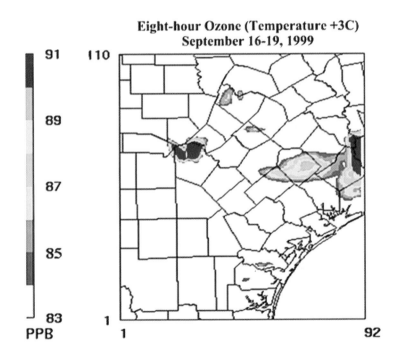

Eight-hour Ozone (Temperature +3C) September 16-19, 1999

Figure 7. Spatial distribution of eight-hour ozone exceedances

Extent of Eight-hour Ozone Exceedances

This analysis represents the number of grid cells or area impacted by eight-hour ozone exceedances with rising temperature perturbations represented by the number of grid cells. As revealed in Figure 8, for the first 2°C (3.60°F) temperature augmentation there is a substantial increase of in area with exceedances relative to the base case for the major portions of the 4 km (2.49 mi) domain. Thereafter, with each degree rise in temperature, the percent increase in the area of eight-hour ozone exceedances relative to the immediately preceding perturbation case declines reinforcing the fact that certain portions of the modeling domain are more affected than others by temperature perturbations.

As expected, the spatial extent of ozone exceedances increases significantly in comparison to the base case with rising temperatures. This increase is linear for correspondingly escalating perturbed temperatures relative to the base case.

Figure 8 also portrays the fact that amongst the NNA regions, the San Antonio counties have the largest number of grid cells or area impacted by the eight-hour ozone exceedances in the base case. The Corpus Christi and Victoria NNA regions have no instances of ozone exceedances in base case. The Corpus Christi region shows a significant increase of number of grid cells with ozone exceedances for the 3 to 6°C (5.40 to 6.80°F) temperature perturbation cases relative to the base case. Overall, the inland areas show a much greater impact with increasing temperature perturbations than the coastal regions which is consistent with the base case results. The percent increase in spatial extent of area with exceedances is linear as well for these urban subregions relative to the base case.

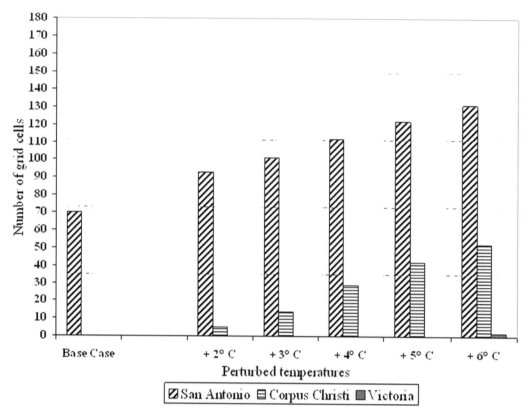

Figure 8. Number of grid cells exceeding eight-hour ozone standard for base case and each temperature perturbed case

The impact of temperature perturbations on surface ozone concentrations was also determined by computing the total number of eight-hour averaged ozone exceedances over the entire 4 km (2.49 mi) modeling domain for the episodic period for each of the temperature perturbation scenarios. The percent increase in number of exceedances relative to base case is almost linear for each consecutive degree rise in temperature (Figure 8). The number of exceedances increases substantially for the first 2°C (3.6°F) rise in temperature in the 4 km (2.49 mi) modeling domain. Subsequently the increase in the number of eight-hour ozone exceedance events is more moderate with respect to the immediately preceding temperature perturbation scenario. This analysis emphasizes the fact that the temperature perturbations affect the number of exceedances in certain grid cells in the modeling domain located mostly in the urban regions.

It is seen (Figure 9) that the San Antonio NNA region is the most affected area amongst the NNAs with 243 eight-hour ozone exceedances in the base case. Corpus Christi does not possess any eight-hour ozone exceedances in the base case, but the number of ozone exceedances in these areas increases significantly with every 1°C (1.8°F) rise in temperatures. Since San Antonio has a large number of exceedances already in the base case, the consequent increase with rise of temperatures is not as substantial as for Corpus Christi. Thus Corpus Christi is more affected by temperature perturbations relative to San Antonio.

Night-time vs. Daytime Temperature Perturbations

In the milieu of climate change, since night-time temperatures have increased at almost twice the rate of daytime temperatures, an ozone sensitivity run was conducted in which daytime temperature was increased by 3°C (5.4°F) and nighttime temperatures was increased by 4.5°C (8.1°F). The results revealed that there was a slight decrease of peak ozone concentrations (about 0.5 ppb) on this occasion from the case where temperatures were increased uniformly by 3°C (5.4°F). The temperature changes at night might impact the NO_3 and/or N_2O_5 reaction rates which actually remove some NO_x from the system more efficiently through formation and deposition of HNO_3, and this would decrease the amount of NO_x available the next day for ozone formation.

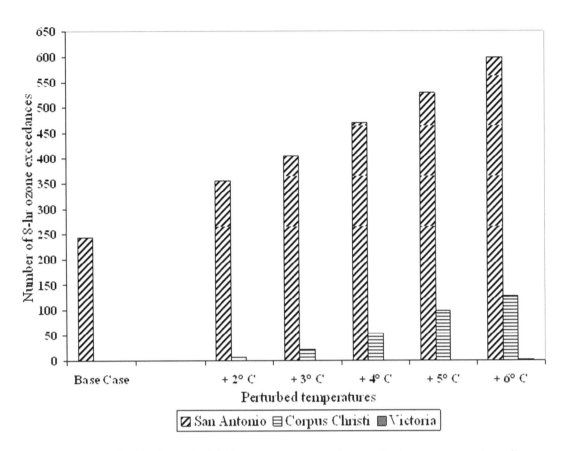

Figure 9. Number of eight-hour ozone exceedances for base case and each temperature perturbed case

Summary

An assortment ozone sensitivity runs were accomplished with different perturbations in temperatures over the South Texas for high ozone days of September 16 to 19, 1999. The results revealed conclusively that global temperature augmentations could significantly impact peak eight-hour ozone concentrations and eight-hour ozone exceedances, especially in the urban regions of South Texas. Transboundary flux enhancements from the industrialized Houston-Galveston region supplement ozone concentrations during the temperature perturbations. These results prove conclusively that potential emission control strategies need to incorporate climate change in their formulation. Climate change can amplify pollution related health effects due to the increase in the number of ozone exceedances. This issue of climate change becomes even more crucial if the eight-hour standards become more stringent in the future as the current eight-hour ozone standards are under scrutiny. The eight-hour NAAQS ozone standards may be further lowered to 60 to 70 ppb to safeguard the health of the sensitive susceptible subpopulation. The lessening of ozone standards will substantially increase spatially the areas under non-attainment of the ozone standards. As seen in this study, climate perturbations will then considerably enhance the already rising number of ozone exceedances as well as expand the area under non-attainment of the eight-hour ozone standards with increasing rise in temperature values. In order to fully assess the effects of climate perturbations in South Texas, additional studies which separately assess potential changes in water vapor and mixing heights, and collectively assess prospective changes in all meteorological variables as a consequence of climate change need to be conducted. This is necessary to obtain a more holistic picture regarding impact of climate change on the regional air quality in South Texas.

Challenges of South Texas Air Quality in 2100

It has been already determined through previous modeling studies (Biswas et al. 2001, Hogrefe et al. 2000) that, in addition to processes on short-term scales such as the diurnal scale (24 hours), longer term processes on the synoptic (2 to 21 days) and baseline scales (greater than 21 days) embracing weather patterns and seasonality play a major role in variability of ozone and its precursor concentrations. Recent studies appear to confirm that processes occurring on global scales such as intercontinental transport of pollutants (Fiore et al. 2002a) influence regional-scale ozone. Therefore, climate change, a global scale process which is expected to occur due to the anticipated growth in global emissions, can impact global tropospheric chemistry (Fiore et al. 2002b), and can therefore alter the chemical composition of the troposphere, intensifying the injurious effects on regional and urban air quality. The increasingly hemispheric nature of air quality problems (Akimoto 2003) linked with global processes brings forth the debate that future emission control strategies cannot be developed in isolation in a particular region. The strategies need to be developed conjunctively with other countries in the northern hemisphere. There are still unanswered scientific questions regarding the changing oxidative capacity of the atmosphere and the relative contribution of emissions from each continent towards this change. Although these aspects present a daunting challenge in regional air quality management of the future for any region, a coordinated approach towards long-term emissions reduction strategies can be developed jointly towards dealing with both future air quality development and climate change in South Texas.

In addition to climate change, land use changes and increasing anthropogenic emissions, which are products of expanding urbanization in South Texas, will add to temperature amplifications (Civerolo et al. 2007). They will play an important role in determining the future air quality. The changing landscape along with the emergence of an urban heat island due to rising temperatures can affect wind patterns especially sea breezes in coastal South Texas region. The present study did not model the effects of increasing urbanization and focused on climate change alone. Coupled modeling systems are necessary to estimate the multifaceted impact of climate, emissions, and land use and their complex interaction in South Texas. The modeling results presented here are of course limited by uncertainties but nevertheless provide a first insight of behavior of air quality under a future climate scenario in South Texas.

Literature Cited

Akimoto H. 2003. Global Air Quality and Pollution. *Science* 302(5651):1716-1719.

Baertsch-Ritter N., J. Keller, J. Dommen, and A. S. H Prevot. 2004. Effects of Various Meteorological Conditions and Spatial Emission Resolutions on the Ozone Concentrations and ROG/NO$_X$ Limitation in the Milan Area (I). *Atmospheric Chemistry and Physics* 4:423-438.

Biswas J. and S. T. Rao. 2001. Uncertainties in Episode Ozone Modeling Stemming from Uncertainties in the Meteorological Fields. *Journal of Applied Meteorology* 40:117 -135.

Biswas, J., C. Hogrefe, S. T. Rao, W. Hao, and G. Sistla. 2002. Evaluating the Performance of Regional-scale Photochemical Modeling Systems: Part III–Precursor Predictions. *Atmospheric Environment* 35:6129-6149.

Chen K. S., Y. T. Ho, C. H.Lai, and Youn-Min Chou. 2003. Photochemical Modeling and Analysis of Meteorological Parameters during Ozone Episodes in Kaohsiung, Taiwan. *Atmospheric Environment* 37:1811-1823.

Civerolo, Kevin, C. Hogrefe, B. Lynn, J. Rosenthal, J. Y. Ku, W. Solecki, J. Cox, C. Small, C. Rosenzweig, R. Goldberg, K. Knowlton, and P. Kinney. 2007. Estimating Effects of Increased Urbanization on Surface Meteorology and Ozone Concentrations in the New York City Metropolitan Region. *Atmospheric Environment* 41:1803-1818.

Constable, J. V. H., A. B. Guenther, D. S. Schimel, and R. K. Monson. 1999. Modeling Changes in VOC Emissions in Response to Climate Change in the Continental United States. *Global Change Biol.* 5:791–806.

Dawson J. P., P. J. Adams, and S. N. Pandis. 2006. Sensitivity of Ozone to Summertime Climate in the Eastern USA: A Modeling Case Study. *Atmospheric Environment* 41:1494- 511.

Dentener F., D. Stevenson, J. Cofala, R. Mechler, M. Amann, P. Bergamaschi, F. Raes, and R. Derwent. 2005. The Impact of Air Pollutant and Methane Emission Controls on Tropospheric Ozone and Fadiative Forcing: CTM Calculations for the Period 1990-2030. *Atmospheric Chemistry and Physics* 5:1731-1755.

Durrenberger C., P. Breitenbach, J. Red, and D. Sullivan. 1999. Development of a Conceptual Model for Episode Selection of High Eight-hour Ozone Events in the Dallas/Fort Worth Area. submitted to AWMA Conference.

ENVIRON International Corporation. 2002. User's Guide Comprehensive Air Quality Model with Extensions (CAMx) Version 3.10. Novato, California: ENVIRON International Corporation.

ENVIRON International Corporation. 2002. Emissions Processing for the Joint CA Photochemical Modeling of Four Southern Texas near Non-Attainment Areas. Report submitted to Texas Commission on Environmental Quality.

Fiore, A. M., D. L. Jacob, I. Bey, R. M. Yantosca, B. D. Field, A. C. Fusco, and J. G. Wilkinson. 2002a. Background Ozone over the United States in Summer: Origin, Trend, and Contribution to Pollution Episodes. *Journal of Geophysical Research* 107(D15):4275, doi:10.1029/2001JD000982.

Fiore, A. M., D. J. Jacob, B. D. Field, D. G. Streets, S. D. Fernandes, and C. Jang. 2002b. Linking Ozone Pollution and Climate Change: The Case for Controlling Methane, *Geophysical Research Letters* 29(19):1919, doi:10.1029/2002GL015601.

Friedlingstein, P., J. L. Dufresne, P. M. Cox, and P. Rayner. 2003. How Positive is the Feedback between Climate Change and the Carbon Cycle? *Tellus Ser. B-Chem. Phys. Meteorol.* 55:692–700.

Grell, G. A., J. Dudhia, and D. R. Stauffer. 1994. A Description of the Fifth Generation Penn State/NCAR Mesoscale Model (MM5), *NCAR Tech. Note*, NCAR TN-398-STR, 138 pp.

Hogrefe C., S. T. Rao, I. G. Zurbenko and P. S. Porter. 2000. Interpreting the Information in Ozone Observations and Model Predictions Relevant to Regulatory Policies in the Eastern United States. *Bulletin of American Meteorological Society* 81:2083-2106.

Hogrefe, C., P. S. Porter, E. Gego, A. Gilliland, R. Gilliam, J. Swall, J. Irwin, and S. T. Rao. 2006. Temporal Features in Observed and Predicted pm$_{2.5}$ Concentrations over the Eastern United States. *Atmospheric Environment* 5041-5055.

Intergovernmental Panel on Climate Change (IPCC). 2007. Climate Change 2007: The Scientific Basis. Cambridge: Cambridge University Press.

Jones J. M, C. Hogrefe, R. F. Henry, J. Ku and G. Sistla. 2005. An assessment of the sensitivity and reliability of the relative reduction factor approach in the development of 8-hr Ozone Attainment Plans. *Journal of Air and Waste Management Association* 55:13-19.

Kim, M., I. Jung and K. John. 2004. Identification of Source Regions Affecting South Texas during the 2002 Haze Event. *Regional and Global Perspectives on Haze: Causes, Consequences and Controversies* Visibility Specialty Conference, October 25-29, 2004, Asheville, NC.

Kumar, Sunil and Kuruvilla John. 2002. Trends in Ozone Levels and Characteristics of High Ozone Episodes in a Semi-Arid Coastal Urban Airshed, *Proceedings of the 95th Annual A&WMA Conference* 6/23-27/02 Baltimore, MD.

Lenton, T. M. 2000. Land and Ocean Carbon Cycle Feedback Effects on Global Warming in a Simple Earth System Model. *Tellus Series B-Chemical Physical Meteorology* 52:1159–1188.

Lindzen, R. S. 1997. Can Increasing Carbon Dioxide cause Climate Change? *Proc. National Academy of Sciences,* U.S.A. 94 (16):8335–8342.

Liu, H., G. Rodriguez. 2005. Human Activities and Global Warming: a Co-integration Analysis. *Environment Model. Software* 20, June 6:761–773.

Manabe, S., R. J. Stouffer. 1993. Century-scale Effects of Increased Atmospheric CO_2 on the Ocean-atmosphere System. *Nature* 364:215–218.

Menut L. 2003. Adjoint Modeling for Atmospheric Pollution Process Sensitivity at Regional Scale. *Journal of Geophysical Research* 108.

Neftel, A., C. Spirig, A. S. H. Prevot, M. Furger, J. Stutz, B. Vogel, and J. Hjorth. 2002. Sensitivity of Photooxidant Production in the Milan Basin: an Overview of Results from EUROTRAC -2 Limitation of Oxidant Production Field Experiment. *Journal of Geophysical Research* 107:D22.

Parrish D. D., J. S. Holloway, M. Trainer, P. C. Murphy, G. L. Forbes, and F. C. Fehsenfeld. 1993. Export of North American Ozone Pollution to the North Atlantic Ocean. *Science* 259:1436-1439.

Plattner, G. K., F. Joos, T. F. Stocker, and O. Marchal. 2001. Feedback Mechanisms and Sensitivities of Ocean Carbon Uptake under Global Warming. *Tellus Series B-Chemical Physical Meteorology* 53:564–592.

Rao, S. T., G. Sistla, and R. F. Henry. 1992. Statistical Analysis of Trends in Urban Ozone Air Quality *Journal of Air & Waste Management Association* 42:1204-1211.

Rao, S. T., I. G. Zurbenko, R. Neagu, P. S. Porter, J. Y. Ku, and R. F. Henry. 1997. Space and Time Scales in Ambient Ozone Data. *Bulletin of the American Meteorological Society* 78:2153–2166.

Russell A. G., and R .Dennis. 2000. NARSTO Critical Review of Photochemical Models and Modeling. *Atmopheric Environment* 34:2283-2324.

Seaman N. L. and S.A. Michelson. 2000. Mesoscale Structure of a High Ozone Episode During the 1995 NARSTO-Northeast study. *Journal of Applied Meteorology* 39:384-398.

Shiohara, N., A. Fernandez-Bremauntz, S. Blanco, and Y. Yanagisawa. 2005. The Commuters' Exposure to Volatile Chemicals and Carcinogenic Risk in Mexico City. *Atmospheric Environment* 39(19):3481–3489.

Sillman S. and P. J Samson. 1995. Impact of Temperature on Oxidant Photochemistry in Urban, Polluted Rural and Remote Environments. *Journal of Geophysical Research* 100:14175-14188.

Szopa, S., D .A. Hauglustaine, R. Vautard, and L. Meenut. 2006. Future Global Tropospheric Ozone Changes and Impact on European Air Quality. *Geophysical Research Letters* 33, Li4805doi: 10.1029/2006GL025860.

U.S.EPA. 1992.User's Guide for the Urban Air Shed Model Volume IV: User's Manual for Emissions Preprocessor System 2.0 *EPA-450/4-90-007D(R)*, Research Triangle Park, NC: U.S. Environmental Protection Agency.

U.S. EPA 1999. Draft Report on the Use of Models and Other Analyses in Attainment for the 8-hour Ozone NAAQS. *EPA-44/R-99-0004,* Research Triangle Park, NC: United States Protection Agency, 27711, 157 pp.

U.S.EPA. 2001. National Air Quality and Emission Trends Report. *EPA 454-R-01-004* http://www.epa.gov/air/aqtrnd99/toc.html 136 (carbon monoxide), 141 (nitrogen oxides), 147 (volatile organic compounds).

UT Austin and ENVIRON. 2004. Report Submitted to Texas Commission on Environmental Quality. Development of the Sept 13-20, 1999 Base Case Photochemical Model for Austin's Early Action Compact.

6

Climate Change Impacts on Water Resources in South Texas

Venkatesh Uddameri and Gomathishankar Parvathinathan

Water is a critical resource which is vital for the sustainable development of semi-arid South Texas. Given limited supplies and already large demands on water, the question of how changes in climate affect the state of water resources in South Texas is on everyone's mind. The focus of this study is a preliminary investigation on how various hydrologic processes are likely to operate within the Mission River Watershed under a plausible climate change scenario. Information obtained from global climate change models indicate that the precipitation is likely to stay constant in 2100 but rainstorms are likely to be more intense. Furthermore, the region is likely to be warmer by about 4°C (7.20°F). Two water balance models: a semi-distributed event-based model covering a time period of twenty-three days following a twenty-two hour rainstorm event, and a lumped monthly water balance model were developed. Having obtained reasonable calibrations, the models were then used in a forecast mode using synthetic data representing precipitation and temperature patterns expected in the year 2100. The event-scale model results indicate that the runoff generated within the watershed will increase with higher rainfall intensification with an estimated peak flow increase of 500 cfs. The results from the monthly water balance model indicate that the projected temperature changes will cause significant increase in evapotranspiration and decreases in soil moisture content and recharge. Reductions in soil moisture may require a potential conversion from dryland farming to irrigation. The reductions in recharge are significant especially during the summer months when the groundwater withdrawals are likely to be the highest. These reductions in recharge will diminish the reliability of groundwater resources as a potential water supply source.

Water Resource Management

Proper management of water resources is an important consideration for sustainable development of South Texas. As discussed in earlier chapters, the rainfall in this semi-arid region exhibits considerable variability and erratically fluctuates between extreme droughts to hurricane-induced storms. The major inland surface water bodies, namely the Rio Grande, Nueces, and San Antonio rivers and the man-made reservoirs in them, occupy less than 2% of the vast land area (about 80,000 sq. km [30888.17 square mi]) often referred to as the South Texas (Figure 1). While average annual rainfall can exceeds 30 inches in some parts, storms tend to be high-intensity, short-duration events that lead to significant runoff and flashfloods. The region's warm climate also causes significant evaporative losses and the potential evapotranspiration is over two times the average annual rainfall (Norwine et al. chapter 2).

Groundwater is another important component of the available water supply in the region. South Texas is largely underlain by the Gulf Coast aquifer. The western sections of the region fall under the Yegua-Jackson and Carrizo-Wilcox formations and the northern sections are underlain by the karstic Edwards aquifer. The water availability in these aquifers varies considerably due to intrinsic geologic heterogeneity and historical use patterns. In addition, groundwater quality is also highly variable and characterized by elevated total dissolved solids (TDS), especially along the coast and in the lower Rio Grande River valley. As such, the estimated groundwater availability exhibits considerable variability as well. Doomsday scenarios of climate change notwithstanding, the high climatic and geologic variability in the region makes quantification of available water supplies an arduous task.

Figure 1. South Texas Area

After being an economically under-served region for decades, South Texas is currently experiencing significant economic growth fueled by the North American Free Trade Agreement (NAFTA) and other policies. The population of the region is expected to double over the next few decades and the once agrarian and ranching economy is transforming into an industrial and service-oriented market of strategic importance. These economic and demographic shifts are going to alter the demands placed on water in years to come. The availability of water in the year 2050 as projected by the Texas Water Development Board (TWDB) as part of their state water planning process is depicted in Figure 2. As can be seen, there are several counties that are expected to fall short of their water requirements around the first half of the century. Effectual water resources management is indeed vital if future generations of South Texans are to have the same access to this natural resource as we have today.

The water demand projections are largely driven by urbanization and other social shifts and do not factor in the impacts of climate change. Given the importance of water to region's sustainability, the central question of how climate change can alter water availability in the future is a major concern to the citizens of South Texas. The primary goal of this study is to make a preliminary attempt to address this concern based on our current understanding of plausible climate change impacts.

Caveat Lector

The only possible approach to assess the impacts of climate change on the state of water resources is through the use of sequential mathematical forecasting tools. The integration of global climate change models with physically based regional water budget models is increasingly being used to forecast and understand climate change impacts on water resources (e.g., Chaplot 2007; Jiang et al. 2007; Fiorillo et al. 2007; Burns et al. 2007 to name a few). Nonetheless, it is important to bear in mind that water balance models in general possess considerable uncertainties due to paucity of data and incomplete understanding of the various processes that affect the movement of water (e.g., Son and Sivapalan 2007). Unfortunately, this concern holds true for regional-scale models developed for South Texas as well (e.g., Chowdhury et al. 2004; Uddameri and Kuchanur 2007). These uncertainties get further exacerbated when inputs (or information) from coarse-scaled global climate change models (GCMs) are used as forcings to these regional-scale water balance models. The admonition of Neils Bohr, "prediction is very difficult,

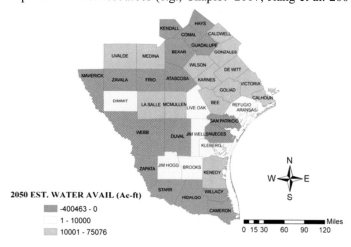

Figure 2. Estimated Water Availibility in 2050

especially if it's about the future," holds very true for the exercise presented here. Nevertheless, it is carried out in the spirit of Roger Bacon's argument that, "more truth arises through error than confusion." It is hoped that the modeling activities pursued in this chapter will generate some initial insights that will initiate a dialogue on this issue and foster further research that will enhance and refine our abilities to address the pressing question of how climate change affects water resources in semi-arid South Texas.

Conceptual Model

Water Balance Modeling

The hydrologic cycle is the fundamental concept behind any water resources investigation and, as such is used as the basis for understanding climate change impacts here as well. A generic conceptualization of the hydrologic cycle is depicted in Figure 3. The hydrologic cycle can be studied over many different spatial scales of interest. First, the region of interest, e.g., South Texas or Mission River Watershed, needs to be demarcated with well defined boundaries which could be natural (e.g.,. watershed) or artificial (e.g., county boundary). This region of interest is referred to as the system of interest or simply a hydrologic system. The hydrologic system of interest such as a watershed in turn consists of several different compartments or sub-systems like aquifers, rivers, lakes, and reservoirs where water accumulates.

The hydrologic cycle is driven by energy derived from the sun that causes moisture recycling. The movement of water through the region is affected by intricate feedback loops between natural phenomenon like precipitation and anthropogenic activities like agriculture and urbanization. In very basic terms, water enters the system of interest through precipitation and is routed into various storage pools such as streams, creeks, rivers, soil, and aquifers.

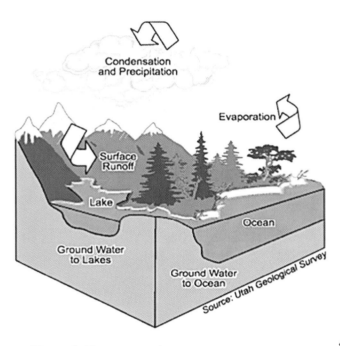

Figure 3. The water cycle

Water also leaves the terrestrial compartment due to a variety of factors such as evaporation from surface water bodies, transpiration from plants, as well as other anthropogenic policies governing water export and import. In addition to these inter-boundary transfers, water is also cycled between various storage pools. For example, in highlands, water from lakes and rivers percolate into the aquifer. Groundwater discharges, also referred to as baseflows, sustain surface water flows in lowlands even during the dry periods. The water budget is a major bookkeeping operation where the flows into and out of the various compartments in a system are tracked. The level of spatial detail is one measure of complexity of the water budget model. A lumped model treats the entire system of interest (watershed) as a single homogeneous entity, while a distributed model divides the system into multiple (sub-watersheds) compartments that are interconnected with one another. Both these approaches can be used for

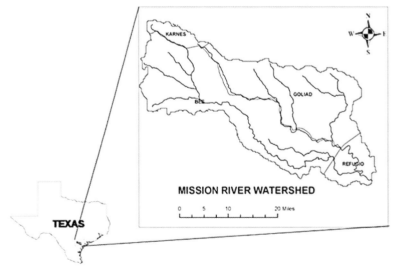

Figure 4. Location of Mission River Watershed

studying the impacts of climate change.

Just as water budgets can be developed at a variety of spatial scales, they can also be built at different time-scales. Hydrologic processes manifest at different time-scales. In arid and semi-arid environments, precipitation occurs intermittently and over a few hours in a month. Associated events like runoff (overland flow) and infiltration (percolation into the soil) occur over several days following the rainfall. On the other hand, evapotranspiration (movement of moisture back into the atmosphere), baseflows (discharges from groundwater) moisture redistribution in the soil and recharge (discharges to groundwater) can manifest over several months following a rainfall event (Stephens 1995). Therefore, water budget models can be developed at multiple temporal scales. Models that are concerned with an individual rainfall event are called "event based models" and are well suited to study runoff characteristics following a rainfall event. On the other hand, models that simulate both wet and dry conditions are known as continuous models. Both these models provide different pieces of information to understand the impacts of climate change on water resources in a region.

Study Area

The Mission River watershed was chosen as a representative system to understand the impacts of climate change on water resources in South Texas. Mission river is a small perennial stream in the coastal bend region of South Texas formed by the confluence of Blanco and Medio creeks (Figure 4). The Mission river watershed has a catchment area of 1787.09 square km (690 square miles) that spans across Refugio, Goliad, Bee, De Witt, and Karnes Counties and drains into the Mission Bay in the Gulf of Mexico. The watershed is underlain by the Gulf Coast aquifer and the water table in the shallower unconfined aquifer is approximately 30 feet below the ground surface in the watershed. There is one gaging station in the watershed[1] operated by the United States Geological Survey (USGS) near the township of Refugio, Texas (NWIS 2004). Monthly precipitation and temperature data are available since 1984 at a weather station operated by the National Weather Service (NWS) near Refugio, Texas (NCDC 2003). Measurements of other hydrologic parameters are rather scanty.

No water rights are allotted for diverting the river flows for municipal, irrigation, and industrial uses from the Mission River or other creeks in the watershed. The western sections of the watershed are mainly classified as rangeland and transitional areas and occupy roughly 15% of the watershed. The southern and eastern sections are used for agriculture (mostly dryland farming) that accounts for nearly 25%. Nearly 57% of the area has been classified as forested. The watershed has been subject to limited urbanization (about 1% urban) and does not contain anthropogenic influences from major cities. Major townships like Refugio in the watershed have maintained fairly stagnant populations in recent decades. These factors greatly minimize the impacts of urbanization on the hydrology of the watershed and make it suitable for studying long-term climatic variations without significantly introducing the confounding effects of urbanization.

Mathematical Models

Event-Scale Assessment

As stated previously water balance models can be run at several spatial and temporal scales. A semi-distributed water balance model for simulating a single rainfall event that occurred on November 3, 2002 was developed using the Soil Moisture Accounting (SMA) model available within the HEC-HMS modeling systems (USACE 2006). The composite rainfall event lasted for a period of twenty-two hours and is depicted in Figure 5. This rainfall was established using NEXRAD (Stage-II) measurements at fourteen different locations scattered over the watershed. These measurements were composited into an effective watershed scale rainfall using the area-weighted Thiessen polygon approach. In addition, spatially distributed pan evaporation rates were obtained from Texas Water Development Board (TWDB) and supplied as model inputs for mean monthly potential evaporation.

Although the SMA model is capable of running in a continuous mode, it was operated in an event mode for this analysis. The SMA model simulates a variety of processes including canopy interception, runoff, soil moisture storage, evapotranspiration from surface water and soil, and deep percolation to groundwater. The theoretical basis of the model has been described in Bennett (1998) and the model is based on concepts derived from linear control

---

[1] Station ID: 08189500

theory. While the original SMA model is a lumped parameter model, the HEC-HMS system allows its application in a semi-distributed mode. To apply the model to the Mission River watershed, three lumped sub-models corresponding to Medio Creek, Blanco Creek, and Mission River sub-watersheds were developed. These sub-watershed models were interconnected using junction elements and outflow from each sub-watershed was routed downstream using the SCS-Lag method (Figure 6). The model was run for a total of twenty-five days at an hourly time-step for a total of six hundred time steps.

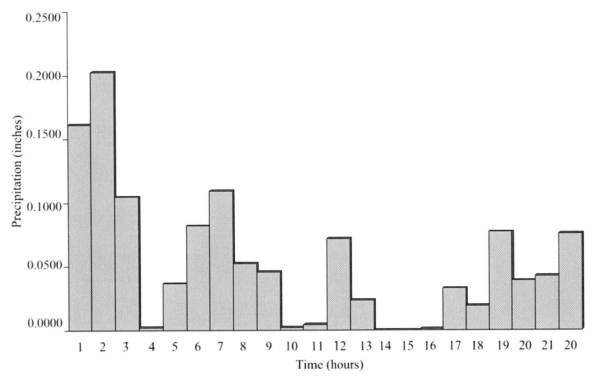

Figure 5. Water Balance Model for November 3, 2002 using the SMA

The model calibration was performed by manually adjusting tension storage and soil storage parameters which are noted to be the two most sensitive model parameters (Fleming and Neary 2004) for each sub-watershed. In addition, the soil percolation coefficient and the SCS-lag coefficient were also mildly adjusted as part of the calibration process as well. An initial estimate for the lag-coefficient was obtained from slopes and land use land cover (LULC) data using HEC-GeoHMS pre-processor (USACE 2003). The residual peak and total flow volume, i.e., the differences between the observed and predicted peak flow and total flow) were used to guide the calibration process. The hourly flow observations for the calibration were obtained from the USGS gaging station on Mission River in Refugio, Texas.

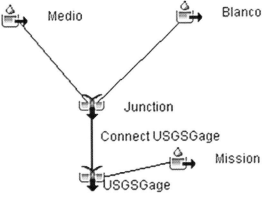

Figure 6. Sub-watershed models

113

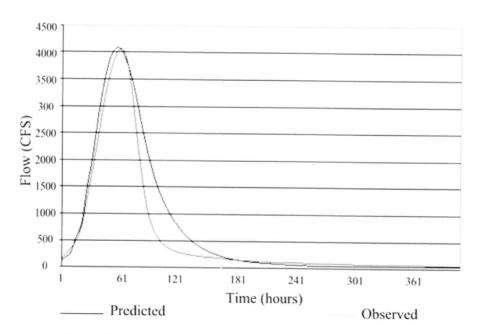

Figure 7. Results of Model Calibration

Table 1. Calibration Statistics

Model Statistics	Values
Observed Peak Flow (CFS)	4062.50
Predicted Peak Flow (CFS)	4048.60
RMSE (CFS)	305.06
Residual Peak Flow (CFS)	13.90
Residual Total Flow (Ac.Feet)	4478.20
Average Abs.Residual (CFS)	120.91
Total Observed Flow (Ac.Feet)	19790.26
Total Predicted Flow (Ac.Feet)	24268.43

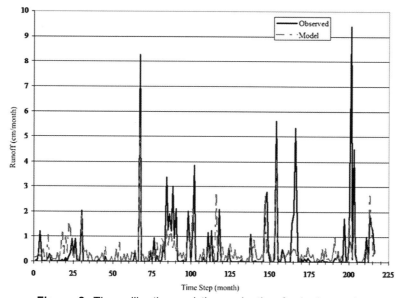

Figure 8. The calibration and the evaluation for hydrograph separated and model predicted runoff

The required model inputs are summarized in Appendix 1, the results of the model calibration are presented in Figure 7 and the calibration statistics are summarized in Table 1. The results indicate the model over-predicts the

total flow by about 22% but does an extremely good job of capturing the peak discharge with an error of less than 0.35%. While better calibrations can possibly be accomplished by simultaneously adjusting other parameters, it is important to bear in mind that the reliability of the model decreases with increasing number of adjustable parameters. Also calibration is an inherently non-unique process (Oreskes et al. 1994) and obtaining excellent calibrations by adjusting a large number of model inputs does not necessarily imply that the model will have good predictive abilities. Therefore, a trade-off between calibration accuracy and the number of adjustable parameters needs to be maintained and evaluated in the context of the accuracy needed for the intended application. From this standpoint the calibration obtained here was deemed reasonable because the model is intended to evaluate the impacts of short-term phenomenon like alterations in peak discharges due to climate change.

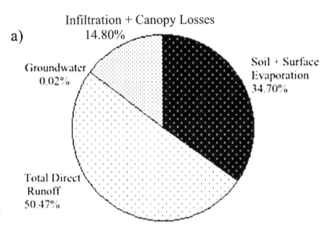

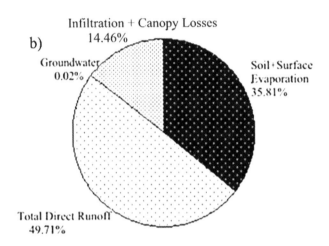

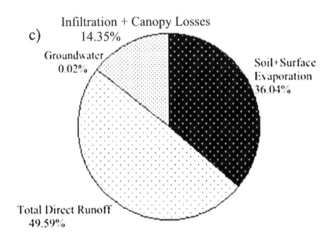

Figure 9 a. b. and c. Rainfall is distributed between different hydrologic compartments when the climate change induces a temperature increase of either two degrees or four degrees over the baseline (current) values.

Monthly Water Balance Model

Water balance models developed at monthly time-step offer a reasonable compromise between computational tractability, data needs, and application requirements and as such have been used for a variety of applications including climate change studies (e.g., Thornthwaite 1948; Haan 1972; Alley 1984; Xu and others 1996; Xu and Singh 1998; Wright and Xu 2000). Recently, a lumped watershed scale monthly water balance model has been developed for the Mission River watershed (Uddameri and Kuchanur 2007). The average monthly soil moisture in the watershed is the master variable in this model capable of simulating infiltration, runoff, deep percolation (recharge to groundwater), soil moisture storage and evapotranspiration. A major challenge in developing monthly water balance in semi-arid and arid watershed lies in the fact that rainfall events tend to be intermittent and occur over short durations (i.e., few hours in a month). The use of an average rainfall (i.e., total monthly rainfall averaged over an entire month) causes an over-estimation of infiltration and an under-estimation (and most times zero) runoff, which is not realistic. To overcome this obstacle, an innovative procedure was developed in that the average rainfall intensity for each month was obtained by dividing the total volume of rainfall observed in each month with an equivalent storm duration period that was obtained via calibration. Preliminary analysis of the available rainfall data indicated while the total rainfall amounts varied between months, the total number of rainfall hours varied little. As such, the storm duration was assumed to stay constant over the entire simulation period to make the model parsimonious. The equivalent rainfall duration was

115

obtained via calibration by matching the rainfall excess predicted by the model to the hydrograph separated rainfall excess. In addition, the field capacity, soil sorptivity, and infiltration constant were also obtained via calibration.

The observations in the time-period (1985 to 1997) were used for calibrating the model and the data from the time-period (1998 to 2002) was used to independently evaluate the model. The calibration was objectively carried using evolutionary genetic algorithms (Goldberg 1989). The mean square error was used as the calibration statistic and the calibration root mean square error (RMSE) was equal to 0.64 cm/month (0.251 in/month) while the RMSE for the evaluation dataset was equal to 1.31 cm/month (0.515 in/month). The required model inputs can be found in Uddameri and Kuchanur (2007) and are not repeated here in the interest of brevity. The calibration and the evaluation for hydrograph separated and model predicted runoff is depicted in Figure 8. The coarse temporal resolution of the model precludes it from capturing the flashiness in the streams caused due to high intensity storms. However, the

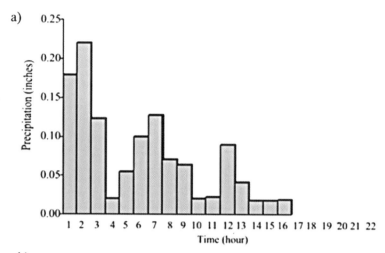

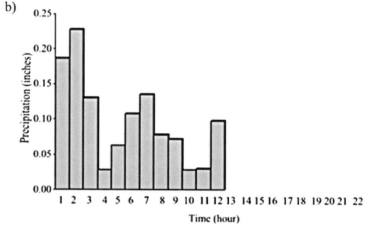

Figure 10 a. and b. The synthetic rainfall events adopted for assessing the impacts of increased rainfall intensity; a) shows time period of sixteen hours and b) shows rainfall for twelve hours.

model is able to better capture the more persistent low flows. The calibration and evaluation RMSE for these persistent flows are 0.591 and 0.458 cm/month (0.233 and 0.180 in/month) respectively. Therefore, this model is suitable for assessing climatic influences of persistent hydrologic parameters such as recharge, evapotranspiration and soil moisture.

Results and Discussion

Effects of Increasing Temperature – Event Scale Analysis

GCM model predictions indicate that the average temperature may increase by about 4°C (7.20°F) in the year 2100. What influence could this temperature raise have on hydrologic factors during a rainfall event? To address this question, the potential evaporation corresponding to increase in temperature was first computed using the following empirical equation developed from available temperature and pan evaporation data:

$$PE = 0.37 x EXP(0.299 x T) \quad \text{Where T is Fahrenheit (R}^2 = 0.91) \quad (1)$$

The water balance results presented in Figures 9 (a-c) depict how the rainfall is distributed between different hydrologic compartments when the climate change induces a temperature increase of either two degrees or four degrees over the baseline (current) values. The results indicate that there is a small increase in the total evaporation from soil and surface water sources which is offset by smaller decreases in the amount of runoff and interception losses. The model predictions also indicate the recharge to groundwater during the twenty-three day simulation period around the twenty-two hour rainfall event is negligible and not influenced by temperature During the actual rainfall event, the relative humidity is nearly 100% and as the atmosphere is saturated with moisture there is negligible evaporation if any. The SMA model does not simulate evaporation when the rainfall is taking place.

The modeling results also indicate that if all other things stay the same, temperature increases are unlikely to affect flooding (peak flow and runoff) characteristics either.

Effects of Increasing Rainfall Intensity – Event Scale Analysis

Many climate change models predict an increase in the rainfall intensity in the twenty-second century (Meehl et al. 2005). Although this result may not be statistically significant in some GCM models, even small changes in rainfall intensity could be of great hydrologic significance. Increased rainfall intensity implies that greater amount of rainfall will be transported as runoff. In the short run, this result implies greater risk of flooding and increases in rainfall intensity will exacerbate any increased runoff due to paving of bare-soils as watersheds undergo urbanization. Increased runoff would also indicate reduced infiltration which in the long run will lead to reduced groundwater recharge and lesser availability of water. To evaluate the impacts of increased rainfall intensity, two synthetic rainfall events were constructed from the baseline case (November 3, 2002). The rainfall volume of these synthetic events was assumed to be equal that of the baseline case (3.023 cm or 1.19 inches). However, the duration of the rainfall was decreased from twenty-two hours to sixteen hours (73% duration) and twelve hours (55% duration) respectively. The synthetic rainfall events adopted for assessing the impacts of increased rainfall intensity are schematically depicted in Figure 10. The rainfall occurring between sixteen to twenty-two hours and twelve to twenty-two hours were uniformly apportioned to earlier periods (i.e., one to sixteen and one to twelve hours respectively) in these scenarios. All other parameters, including potential evapotranspiration rates were unchanged in these model runs. The hydrographs generated at the Refugio USGS gage station under these scenarios (Figure 11) indicated that the peak flow increased from nearly 4000 cfs to 4500 cfs. Also the differences in the peak flow between the 73% duration rainfall and 55% duration rainfall event were fairly small. This result indicates that an increased peak flow is to be expected with increasing rainfall intensity regardless of the magnitude of the predicted change. However, the magnitude of the change may be subject to some threshold effect (i.e., the increase peak flow may plateau off after a certain rainfall intensity).

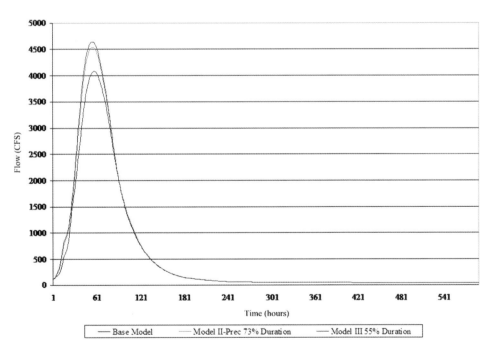

Figure 11. Hydrographs generated at the Refugio USGS gage station under the scenario of the rainfall occurring between sixteen to twenty-two hours and twelve to twenty-two hours

Based on empirical geomorphological relationships (Leopold and Maddock 1953; Chapra 1996), this increase in the peak flow could roughly translate to an increase in water level of one to two feet in the river. Therefore increasing rainfall intensity caused by climate change has the possibility of inundating some low-lying areas of the watershed. Urbanization in the future is likely to enhance the impacts of this flooding and therefore future land use activities must be planned carefully to avoid potentially deleterious flooding impacts.

The water budget analysis for the three rainfall intensity conditions are depicted in Figure 12a - 12c. As can be seen, the increase in the runoff brought forth by increased rainfall intensity is compensated largely by reductions in infiltration, canopy losses, and to a lesser extent by evaporative losses. This result is again to be expected because evaporation activity is curtailed during precipitation due to saturated moisture conditions in the atmosphere. While the recharge to groundwater is not significantly affected during the rainfall event (small changes in the graphs are due to round-off), reduced infiltration implies that lesser water will be available for moisture re-distribution and diffuse recharge that occur long after the cessation of rainfall event.

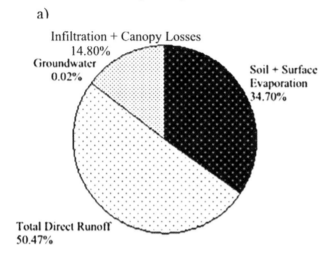

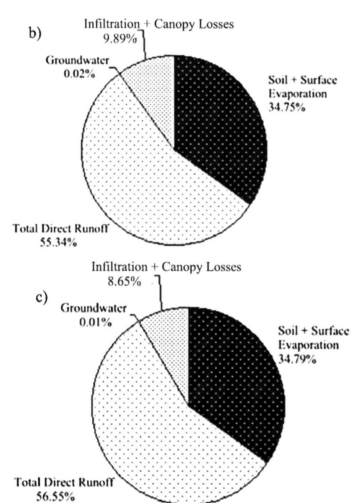

Figure 12 a. b. and c. The water budget analysis for the three rainfall intensity conditions

Impacts of Increasing Temperature – Long-Term Evapotranspiration Effects

While long-term shifts in temperature may not have significant impacts on event-scale water balance, they are more likely to influence long-term hydrologic phenomenon that occur during the dry times. In particular, the impacts are likely to be more pronounced on long-term evapotranspiration as well as diffuse recharge to groundwater. The monthly water balance model used in this study uses the Thornthwaite correlation to estimate potential evapotranspiration and is driven by mean monthly temperature and average length of the day as forcings. This potential evapotranspiration is then employed to estimate actual evapotranspiration using a linear function described by Bras and Cordova (1982) and Rodriguez-Iturbe et al. (1999). The baseline (1987 to 2002) average potential and actual monthly evapotranspiration and the predicted change when the temperature in each month is raised by 4°C (7.2°F) is presented in Figure 13. Several observations can be made from Figure 13. The potential evapotranspiration is likely to increase significantly by at least 0.1 ft/month (0.03 m/month) to over 0.175 ft/month (0.53 m/month) during summer months. However, the differences in actual evapotranspiration are not as dramatic and are about 0.05 ft/month (0.015 m/month). This small change still translates to roughly 265,000 ac-ft/yr of excess water that is lost via evapotranspiration. As a comparison, the projected water demand for the city of San Antonio for the year 2010, not 2100, is close to 230,000 ac-ft/yr and in year 2050 it is close to 360,000 ac-ft/yr (TWDB 2007).

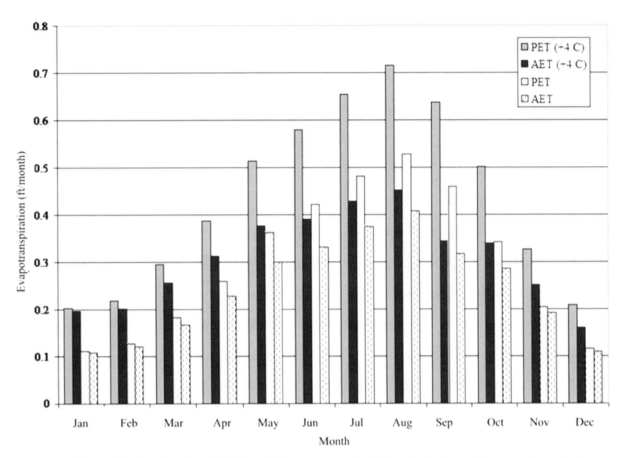

Figure 13. The baseline (1987 to 2002) average potential and actual monthly evapotranspiration and the predicted change when the temperature in each month is raised by 4°C (7.2°F)

Evapotranspiration in the watershed is primarily due to vegetation and during periods of stresses, plants do exhibit the ability to conserve water by closing their stomata through which water is lost to the atmosphere (Rodriguez-Iturbe et al. 1999). Increased periods of dryness as predicted by GCM will cause more frequent periods of stresses on vegetation and may possibly diminish the ability of some plants to quick changes (fatigue situations). Some plants may be better adaptors to these changes in stress patterns and may survive and compete better than others for available moisture. Therefore, climate changes can alter the vegetation makeup of the watershed, which in turn will affect the amount of evapotranspiration. The present analysis does not include these climate-biotic interaction possibilities, and it assumes that the vegetative make-up of the watershed is not altered significantly due to climatic and urbanization influences.

Impacts of Increasing Temperature – Long-Term Soil Moisture Effects

The impact of increasing temperature on soil moisture is schematically depicted in Figure 14. As can be seen, the average soil moisture in the watershed will decrease with increasing temperatures assumed to prevail in 2100. However, the changes in the soil moisture are not as significant in the later winter and spring months, i.e., the early part of the year. However, decreasing trends will start during the summer months and continue through fall and early winter months. The soil moisture will decrease by about 5% to 20% on average and, based on the simulated values, it does not appear like there will be significant critical deficits that could cause wilting of plants and other deleterious effects. However, the model results represent only a broad-brush assessment. Wilting and other soil moisture-driven stress on ecology could take place locally within the watershed. However, the decreases noted could hamper dryland farming in the watershed and increase the need for irrigation.

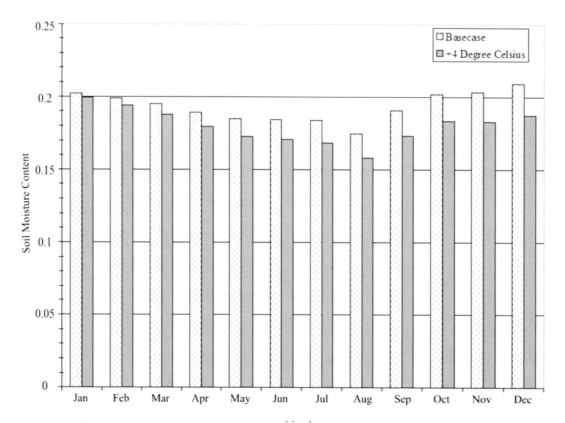

Figure 14. Average monthly recharge for the baseline and year 2100 conditions

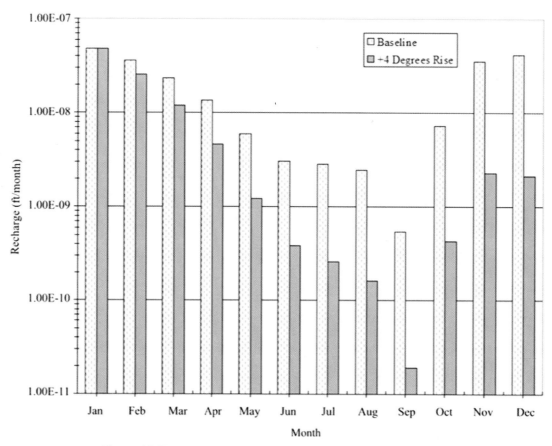

Figure 15. The impact of increasing temperature on soil moisture

Impacts of Increasing Temperature – Long-Term Recharge Effects

The recharge in the monthly water balance model was computed using the Darcy-Buckhingham equation (Stephens 1995). The constitutive capillary-pressure-saturation relationships were based on the Campbell model (Clapp and Hornberger 1982). The average monthly recharge for the baseline and year 2100 conditions are presented in Figure 15 where it can be seen that the increase in temperature can have a major impact on estimated recharge. The simulation results indicate that recharge could be decreased roughly by an order-of-magnitude especially during the summer months. Groundwater resources are going to be a major source of freshwater for Texas in years to come and some plans are underway to develop groundwater in the vicinity of the watershed to meet regional demands in the near future. Urbanization of the South Texas region and this watershed in particular will also reduce recharge to the aquifer. Groundwater resources are generally considered more reliable than surface water sources in that they are not as affected by droughts and other similar vagaries of nature (Tsur 1990). However, the results obtained here indicate that this reliability could be diminished due to potential climate change effects.

Summary and Conclusions

The primary goal of this study was to develop preliminary insights aimed at addressing the pressing question about the state of water resources in South Texas based on the predicted climate in 2100. Forecasts from an ensemble of global atmosphere ocean climate change models appear to indicate that the region will be warmer by about 4.0°C (7.2°F) in 2100. Also, the average precipitation is not likely to vary significantly but rainstorms may be of higher intensity and shorter duration. These changes can cause alterations to both short-term (runoff) and long-term (evapotranspiration and recharge) hydrologic phenomena. The impacts of climate changes on these hydrologic processes were evaluated at the Mission River watershed in South Central Texas using a semi-distributed event-based model and a lumped monthly water balance model. These models were first calibrated for current conditions using available historical data collected both in-situ and via remote-sensing. Having obtained satisfactory calibrations, the models were then run in a forecast mode to simulate synthetic storm events and temperature conditions representative of the potential climate in the year 2100.

The results from the event-based model indicate that, for the rainfall event studied and the climate change conditions assumed, plausible increases in temperature are unlikely to cause significant changes in hydrologic variables. However, runoff generated within the watershed will increase when the same amount of rain will fall in a shorter time-period. Model results indicate that the peak flow could increase by about 500 cfs, and this increase could cause the water levels in the river to rise by about one to two feet, thereby increasing flooding and inundation possibilities in the low-lying areas of the watershed.

The results from the monthly water balance model indicate that the projected temperature changes will cause significant increase in evapotranspiration and decreases in soil moisture content and recharge. The amount of water lost via evapotranspiration is slightly higher than the current water demands of the city of San Antonio. Reductions in soil moisture will likely require a potential conversion from dryland farming to irrigation. The reductions in recharge are significant especially during the summer months when the groundwater withdrawals are likely to be the highest. These reductions in recharge will diminish the reliability of groundwater resources to supply water for various anthropogenic needs.

The total changes in the water resources within a watershed are a function of both long-term climate change and short-term urbanization. In many cases, the long-term climate change will exacerbate the deleterious urbanization impacts that take place in the short term. For example, paving of bare soils due to urbanization will increase the amount of runoff and flooding in the same way as the intensification of storms due to climate change. Similarly, increased urbanization could result in greater groundwater withdrawals and will exacerbate the effects brought forth by climate change shifts that lead to increased evapotranspiration, decreased soil moisture storage and recharge. It is important to remember that while urbanization and climate change occur concurrently, the present exercise did not model the effects of urbanization and focused on climate change alone. Uncertainties in model predictions arise due a variety of factors including limited data availability; incomplete understanding of hydrologic processes; theoretical gaps and controversies; and also due to the need to estimate certain inputs via calibration which is inherently a non-unique process. All the uncertainties in the global climate change models get imported into the water budget models, which are uncertain by themselves. Also, any insights generated from these combined models will be affected by the uncertainties in both the climate change and water budget models. Therefore, every effort was made to obtain reasonable and reliable calibrations and site-specific inputs. A comprehensive uncertainty analysis could however not be carried out with the current scope but it is planned for the future. These limitations notwithstanding, the results provide a first glimpse of how various hydrologic processes affecting water resources in the watershed behave under a future climate scenario.

Acknowledgments

Funding for this study was provided by the National Oceanic and Atmospheric Administration – Environmental Entrepreneurship Program (NOAA-EEP) through a cooperative agreement grant to the Texas A&M University-Kingsville (V. Uddameri, PI).

Literature Cited

Alley, W. M. 1984. On the Treatment of Evapotranspiration, Soil Moisture Accounting and Aquifer Recharge in Monthly Water Balance Models. *Water Resources Research* 20:1137-1149.

Bennett, T. 1998. Development and Application of a Continuous Soil Moisture Accounting Algorithm for the Hydrologic Engineering Center Hydrologic Modeling System ~HEC-HMS. Dept. of Civil and Environmental Engineering., Univ. of California, Davis.

Bras, R. and J. Cordova. 1981. Intra-seasonal Water Allocation in Deficit Irrigation. *Water Resources Research* 17: 866-874.

Burns, D. A., Julian Klaus, and Michael R. McHale. 2007. Recent Climate Trends and Implications for Water Resources in the Catskill Mountain Region New York, USA. *Journal of Hydrology* 336(1-2):155-170.

Chaplot, V. 2007. Water and Soil Resources Response to Rising Levels of Atmospheric CO_2 Concentration and to Changes in Precipitation and Air Temperature. *Journal of Hydrology* 337(1-2):159-171.

Chapra, S. 1996. *Surface Water Quality Modeling* New York, NY: McGraw Hill.

Chowdhury, A. H., S. Wade, R.Emace, and C. Ridgeway. 2004. *Groundwater Availability Model of the Central Gulf Coast Aquifer System: Numerical Simulations through 1999* Austin, TX; Texas Water Development Board. 108pp,

Clapp, R. B. and G. M. Hornberger. 1978. Empirical Equations for Some Soil Hydraulic Properties. *Water Resources Research* 14:601-604.

Fiorillo, F., Libera Esposito, and Francesco M. Guadagno. 2007. Analyses and Forecast of Water Fesources in an Ultra-centenarian Spring Discharge Series from Serino (Southern Italy). *Journal of Hydrology* 336(1-2):125-138.

Fleming, M. and V. S. Neary. 2004. Continuous Hydrologic Modeling Study with HMS. *Journal of Hydrologic Engineering* 9(3):175-183.

Goldberg, D. E. 1989. *Genetic Algorithms in Search, Optimization, and Machine Learning.* Lebanon: Addison-Wesley Professional.

Jiang, T., Yongqin David Chen, Chong-yu Xu, Xiaohong Chen, Xi Chen, and Vijay P. Singh. 2007. Comparison of Hydrological Impacts of Climate Change Simulated by Six Hydrological Models in the Dongjiang Basin, South China. *Journal of Hydrology* 336(3-4):316-333.

Leopold, L. B., T. Maddock. 1953. The Hydraulic Geometry of Stream Channels and Some Physiographic Implications. *U.S. Geological Survey Professional Paper 252.*

Meehl, G. A., Julie, M. Arblaster, and Claudia Tebaldi. 2005. Understanding Future Patterns of Increased Precipitation Intensity in Climate Model Simulations. *Geophysical Research Letters* 32:1-4.

NCDC. 2003. National Climatic Data Center, http://www.ncdc.noaa.gov. 2007.

NWIS. 2004. National Water Information System, http://www.ncdc.noaa.gov. 04/2007.

Oreskes, N., K. Shrader-Frechette, and K. Belitz. 1994. Verification, Validation and Confirmation of Numerical Models in the Earth Sciences. *Science* 263:641-646.

Rodriguez-Iturbe, I., P. D'Odorico, et al. 1999. On the Spatial and Temporal Links between Vegetation, Climate, and Soil Moisture. *Water Resources Research* 35:3709-3722.

Son, K. and M. Sivapalan. 2007. Improving Model Structure and Reducing Parameter Uncertainty in Conceptual Water Balance Models through the Use of Auxiliary Data. *Water Resources Research* 43(1).

Stephens, D. B. 1995. *Vadose Zone Hydrology.* Boca Raton: CRC.

Swartzendruber, D. and E. G. Youngs. 1974. A Comparison of Physically-based Infiltration Equations. *Soil Science* 117:165-167.

Thornthwaite, C. W. 1948. An Approach Toward a Rational Classification of Climate. *Geographic Review* 38:55-94.

Tsur, Y. 1990. The Stabilization Role of Groundwater when Surface Water Supplies are Uncertain: the Implications for Groundwater Development. *Water Resources Research* 26(5):811-818.

TWDB. 2007. *Water for Texas 2007.*

Uddameri, V. and M. Kuchanur. 2007. Estimating Aquifer Recharge in Mission River Watershed, Texas: Model Development and Calibration using Genetic Algorithms. *Environmental Geology* 51(6): 897-910.

USACE. 2003. *Geospatial Hydrologic Modeling System HEC-GeoHMS User's Manual.*

USACE. 2006. *Hydrologic Modeling System HEC-HMS User's Manual.*

Wright, K. A. and Y. Xu. 2000. A Water Balance Approach to the Sustainable Management of Groundwater in South Africa. *Water SA* 26:167-170.

Xu C. Y. and S. Halldin. 1996. Regional Water Balance Modeling in the NOPEX Area: Development and Application of Monthly Water Balance Models. *Journal of Hydrology* 180:211-236.

Xu C-Y. 1998. A Review on Monthly Water Balance Models for Water Resource Investigations. *Water Resources Management* 12:31-50.

Zheng, Y. Q., Z. C. Qian, H. R. He, H. P. Liu, X. M. Zeng, and G. Yu. 2007. Simulations of Water Resource Environmental Changes in China During the Last 20,000 Years by a Regional Climate Model. *Global and Planetary Change* 55(4): 284-300.

APPENDIX 1

Table 2. HEC-HM Model Parameters

Parameters	Blanco	Medio	Mission
Canopy (%)	60.6	53.24	56.63
Surface (%)	0	0	0
Soil (%)	38.6	38.68	8.37
Groundwater 1 (%)	50	50	50
Groundwater 2 (%)	50	50	50
Canopy Storage (in)	0.1	0.1	0.1
Surface Storage (in)	0.06	0.06	0.06
Maximum Infiltration (in/hr)	0.42	0.44	0.52
Impervious (%)	2.52	2.9	16.75
Soil Storage (in)	0.46	0.47	0.51
Tension Storage (in)	0.42	0.42	0.31
Soil Percolation (in/hr)	0.05	0.01	0.05
Groundwater 1 Storage (in)	0.02	0.02	0.02
Groundwater 1 Percolation (in/hr)	0.05	0.05	0.05
Groundwater 1 Coefficient (hr)	918	918	918
Groundwater 2 Storage (in)	0	0	0
Groundwater 2 Percolation (in/hr)	0	0	0
Groundwater 2 Coefficient (hr)	0	0	0
SCS Lag Time (mins)	2758	2825	318

7

Climate Change for South Texas and Water Resource Impacts: A Specific Focus on the Agriculture Sector

Kim Jones and Irama Wesselman

Introduction

A major impact closely linked with climate change has always been projected to be increases in evapotranspiration (ET). The increase in ET can cause an increased demand for water resources in order to maintain stable agricultural and horticultural production. In semi-arid South Texas, this is already a critical issue. Evapotranspiration occurs as vegetation takes up water, uses the water for nutrient adsorption and cell transport, and releases or transpires the water back into the atmosphere. Predictive models coupled with historical data records suggest that higher carbon dioxide (CO_2) levels and temperature will increase evapotranspiraton (ET) rates, which impacts the hydrologic cycle in some proportion to the predicted temperature increase. All ET models link the rate of ET to temperature and other factors such as solar radiation, wind speed, relative humidity, and other parameters. Another complexity to consider is the coupling of CO_2 increases with an increase in photosynthesis which can reduce ET but also cause increased water demand through the root system growth. This process change will cause a reduction in atmospheric water vapor, which in turn leads to an amplification of the greenhouse effect and can cause a spiral toward even higher global temperatures. Unfortunately, none of these effects can be completely uncoupled from the more dramatic effects of urbanization and the impacts of population growth and the resulting needs, in the form of agriculture and municipal water use pressures on water demand. Thus, the predictive models for water resource impacts due to climate change will always be limited due to the uncertainty in the response of societal and anthropogenic changes and trends due to their interaction with the plant biomes within the ecosystem. Will more land be cleared and converted to agriculture? Will genetically engineered plant materials cause changes in ET trends through even higher water consumption? Accepting the limitations of the lack of knowledge about those responses, some predictive estimates based on studies such as the NCAR projections can still be possible with the information we have now.

Approximately 70% of the water extracted from groundwater and surface water resources are used to provide irrigation for agricultural applications around the globe (Magee 2005). The region of South Texas is no different. Water resource demands for a large agricultural region such as the Lower Rio Grande Valley are under great stress at the present time. The Texas portion of the Lower Rio Grande Valley alone is expected to grow in population from 900,000 in the year 2000 to over 2,100,000 in the year 2050 (LRGV Integrated Water Resource Plan 1999). The major water demand category in this region is agriculture with over 85% of the water use coming from that sector (1.4 million acre-feet in 2000). This does not include the increase in demand from the Mexican side of the international boundary. Even though some of this land will be taken out of agricultural use over time as municipal growth continues, municipal water demand is expected to increase from 212, 000 acre-feet in 2000 to over 403,000 acre-feet in 2050.

Evapotranspiration Models

Based on the projections of temperature and precipitation from the NCAR model, the impacts on ET and irrigated agriculture were modeled and evaluated. The sensitivity of ET to air temperature changes was evaluated using the Thornwaite equation. This simpler equation for ET was selected as an approximation because the equation is based only on an exponential relationship between mean monthly temperature and latitude data.

$$ETu = 0.63 \ (10t_C/I)^a$$

where $a = 0.000000675(I)^3 - 0.000077(I)^2 + 0.01792(I) + 0.49239$

I = temperature efficiency index, an integral element of the Thornwaite's classification of climate, is the sum of 12 monthly values of the heat index $I = (t_C/5)^{1.514}$

t_C = temperature in degrees, Centigrade

ETu = unadjusted potential evapotranspiration

Then a more accurate estimate of ET or adjusted ET can be determined.

$$ETa = N \times ETu$$

ETa = adjusted potential evapotranspiration

N = monthly adjustment factor related to hours of daylight

To validate such an estimation procedure, the prediction of ETa or Potential Evapotranspiration (PET) from the model was compared to the data of Enciso and Wiedenfeld (2005) and found to be reasonable in its approximation.

Table 1. Comparison of monthly PET estimate by utilizing the Thornwaite equation with PET from Enciso and Wiedenfeld (2005)

	Jan	Feb	Mar	Apr	May	Jun	Jul	Aug	Sep	Oct	Nov	Dec	Annual Total (in)
PET	2.61	2.87	4.18	4.98	6.14	6.62	6.98	6.81	5.77	4.79	3.51	2.73	57.99
PET Enciso	3.34	3.74	5.00	5.91	7.13	7.20	7.80	7.48	5.83	4.92	3.82	3.11	62.24

Thus the PET calculated by using Thornwaite equation produced results very similar to the historical data estimated from Enciso and Wiedenfeld (2005) where the historical PETs were measured over a nine-year period for the Lower Rio Grande Valley Area. This validation led to the conclusion that additional predictive work could continue with the simple model for PET.

Results and Discussion

The results of PET estimated by the Thornwaite method are shown below in Figure 1 for increases in model temperature as projected by the NCAR model.

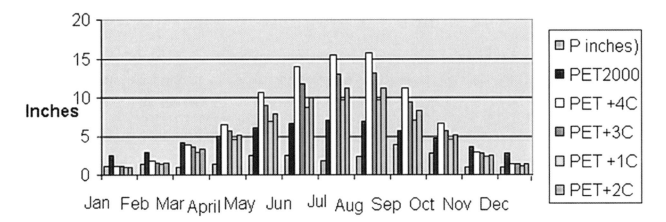

Figure 1. Monthly PET Estimate with temperature increases of 1ºC, 2ºC, 3ºC and 4ºC. PET 2000 was calculated based on US National Climatic Data from 1970 -2000.

Table 1 is a numerical summary of the PET increases showing the total projected annual changes based on the temperature increase results from the NCAR model.

Table 2. Summary of percentage PET change for 1ºC, 2ºC, 3ºC, and 4ºC temperature increases.

	Jan	Feb	Mar	April	May	Jun	Jul	Aug	Sep	Oct	Nov	Dec	Annual Total (inches)	PET Change %
P inches	1.2	1.37	0.95	1.36	2.51	2.49	1.7	2.31	4	2.76	0.95	1.01	22.61	
PET (in)	2.61	2.87	4.18	4.98	6.14	6.62	6.98	6.81	5.77	4.79	3.51	2.73	57.99	
PET+1C	1.01	1.39	2.97	4.51	6.94	8.70	9.62	9.59	7.15	4.55	2.28	1.16	59.88	3.26
PET+2C	1.06	1.49	3.25	5.03	7.78	10.01	11.11	11.10	8.18	5.09	2.48	1.39	68.06	17.36
PET+3C	1.13	1.59	3.59	5.67	9.06	11.68	13.03	13.05	9.50	5.76	2.72	1.31	78.06	34.66
PET+4C	1.19	1.72	4.00	6.47	10.57	13.87	15.56	15.61	11.20	6.60	3.00	1.40	91.20	57.26

Thus, a projected increase of almost 60% in ET water demand for the region is likely and very reasonable based on historical trends.

The monthly PET was also estimated with a systems model using VENSIM® PLE to estimate the PET change over the temporal model period of a hundred years. The model and the results of simulation are presented below:

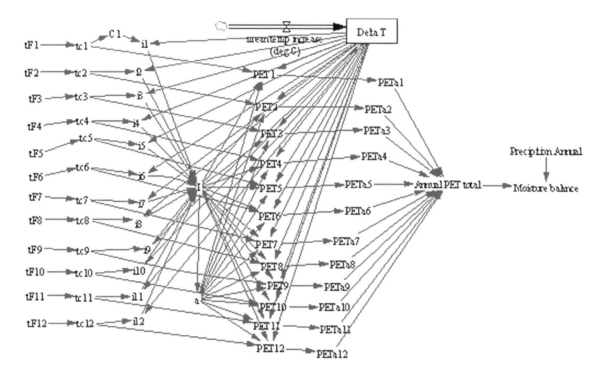

Figure 2. VENSIM® PLE systems diagram showing the twelve-month simulation approaches resulting in an annual PET estimate over one hundred years of temperature

Figure 2 shows the systems diagram for the twelve months of variation each year modeled with a change in average ambient temperature. The Thornwaite model was again used within annual time steps to simulate monthly PET values from the year 2000 up to the year 2100. The model still assumed that the average annual precipitation remained unchanged.

Figure 3 presents plots of the moisture balance decreases and PET increases in units of inches/yr from the simulations for the NCAR model temperature forecast. The model results show the gradual but pronounced exponential rise in PET as predicted by the Thornwaite ET model. The moisture balance in Figure 3 is simply the difference between the annual precipitation minus the predicted annual PET. The area around the Lower Rio Grande Valley shows a deficit of 32 inches/yr of water if the climate temperature increases 4°C from current conditions by the year 2100. A model such as this would typically be used as a guideline for irrigation scheduling as many watering decisions in the agriculture sector are based on PET estimates.

Model Summary and Other Impacts

In summary, an increase of over 50% in water demand in the agriculture sector for a region similar to the Lower Rio Grande Valley of Texas would be a reasonable projected impact based on the climactic changes predicted by the NCAR model through 2100. This does not account for increased demand in the municipal use sector, which will only add to the strain on the water resource allocations. Water demand is projected to reach over 2 million acre feet for the region by 2050, and new resources of over 500,000 acre feet more than current supplies will be needed to meet this demand. The climate change prediction adds even more stress to regional growth with a projected increase of additional 300,000 acre feet to make up for the expected losses to higher evapotranspiration. The increased demand and water shortfall would be even higher if agricultural land is not reduced by 50% over this period as predicted by Rio Grande Valley planners (Perez, Freese and Nichols 1999). Again, complexities such as CO_2 increases in more complex climate change models along with the integration of factors such as relative humidity and solar flux alterations may allow for better predictions and estimated impacts on water resources. However, the simpler models have been proven reliable in many cases and the historical data trends for the Lower Rio Grande Valley suggest these model impacts are at least reasonable and, at worst, some cause for serious concern. The overall impact of such changes is still a matter of debate. An analysis by Vorosmarthy et al. (2000)

determined that while 20% of the increased demand for water resources could be attributed to climate change, a full 80% of the projected demand stress on these resources is likely to be due to the increase in population and urbanization.

Another critical but extremely complex aspect of water resources linked to climate change, especially for South Texas, may be the effect on water quality. While the precise effects and trends for water quality in South Texas are outside the scope of this work, some reasonable expectations in this area can be discussed.

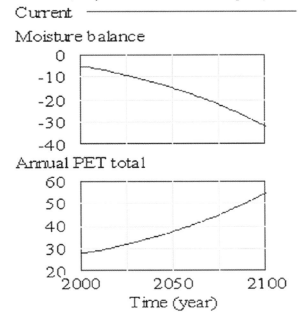

Current

Moisture balance

Annual PET total

Time (year)

Precipition Annual
Current: 22.61

Figure 3. Temporal ET annual trend (inches/yr) as predicted for simulations using an annual time step and the NCAR model temperature profile.

Urbanization impacts routinely cause increased loadings of nutrients and solids from stormwater runoff during intense precipitation events. While many climate change models are predicting only small fluctuations in total annual precipitation amounts, the frequency and intensity of the precipitation events are predicted to experience wider variations in most scenarios. Most models such as the Generalized Watershed Loading Function (GWLF) model developed by Haith and Shoemaker (1987) would generate increased nitrogen and phosphorous loadings from these more intense events. The predicted result would be increased loadings to surface waters due to runoff, leaching, and erosion processes. The extent of the increased loadings and water quality impairment would be based on very localized site specific conditions. Changes in technology and environmental policy toward municipal discharges and agriculture could reduce loadings in some cases. Additionally, CO_2 enrichment from climate change could actually lead to expansion of some agriculture sectors, which could lead to falling prices and some regional crop rotation alterations (Abler et al. 2002).

Groundwater resources are a very significant water supply source for the Coastal Bend of Texas, drawing primarily from the Gulf Coast Aquifer geologic unit. However, the water quality of the resource can be variable on a spatial basis throughout the region. The groundwater quality ranges from very fresh (low total dissolved solids [TDS] < 1000 mg/L) in northern Refugio County all the way to high TDS almost brackish water in Cameron County near the Rio Grande Valley. Historical trends for dissolved solids or water quality parameter degradation almost invariably increase with increased withdrawals or pumpage over time primarily because of increased mineral contents in the lower zones of typical aquifer formations as these drainage units are drawn down (Hibbs 1999; Andren 2001). Another unknown impact on gulf coast aquifers would be salt water intrusion which can result from increase levels of inland pumpage near coastal areas. If climate change causes reduced precipitation and increased evaporation in some areas, and aquifer recharge volumes are reduced, the consequences would likely be a reduction in water quality and increase in dissolved solids and salts. The magnitude of such changes in water quality would be exceedingly difficult to predict and probably have more site specific impacts, however their effect on the efficiency of irrigation and a potential build up of salts in irrigated soils could further inhibit agricultural productivity. A significant limitation of any of the predictive work in this chapter is the lack of inclusion of the urbanization effects on water demand, use and reuse and its interplay with agricultural water demands for the region. However, this limitation could be overcome with a more rigorous model development which incorporates predictions of regional urban growth patterns, crop rotation patterns, agricultural trends and precipitation variations in the future.

Literature Cited

Abler D., J. Shortle, J. Carmichael, and R. Horan. 2002. Climate Change, Agriculture, and Water Quality in the Chesapeake Bay Region , Climatic Change, v55(3): 339-359.

Andren, A. 2001. Groundwater Drawdown, Wisconsin Water Resources Institute accessed at http://www.wri.wisc.edu/GroundwaterDrawdown.pdf, March 2007.

Enciso, J., and B. Wiedenfield. 2005. Irrigation Guidelines Based On Historical Weather Data in the Lower Rio Grand Valley of Texas, Agriculture Water Management. 76:1-7.

Dinpashoh Y. 2006. Study of Reference Crop Evapotranspiration in I.R. of Iran, Agriculture Water Management, 84:123-129.

Haith, D.A. and L. L. Shoemaker. 1987. Generalized Watershed Loading Functions for Stream Flow Nutrients. Water Resources Bulletin. 23(3):471-478.

Hibbs, B. 1999. Hydrogeologic and water quality issues along the El Paso/Juarez Corridor; an international case study, Environmental and Engineering Geoscience. 5(1): 27-39.

Magee, Michael. 2005. Healthy Waters, Bronxville, NY: Spencer Books.

McKenney, M. S. and N. J. Rosenberg.1993. Sensitivity of Some Potential Evapotranspiration Estimation Methods to Climate Change, Agricultural and Forest Meteorology 64:81-110.

Perez, Freese and L. L. C.Nichols. 1999. Integrated Water Resource Plan: Lower Rio Grande Valley Development Council, Report Summary. Technical Report.

Smith K. 1964. A Long Period Assessment of The Penman and Thornwaite Potential Evapotranspiration Formulae, Journal of Hydrology. 2:277-290.

Vorosmarty, C.J. et al., Global Water Resources: Vulnerability from Climate Change and Population Growth, Science, 289.

8

Apparent Rapid Range Change in South Texas Birds: Response to Climate Change?

John H. Rappole, Gene W. Blacklock, and Jim Norwine

At least seventy species of birds native to tropical, subtropical, or warm desert habitats have shown evidence of northward or eastward extension of their breeding distribution into, within, or beyond the borders of South Texas, ranging from a few to several hundred km over a relatively brief time period (decades). Documentation of these changes in distribution for most species is based largely on sightings rather than specimens of nests, eggs, or young. Nevertheless, the changes are in line with regional climatic warming and possible drying, reported by climatologists in Chapters One and Two of this book, which is anticipated to have an ecological effect over the next century roughly similar to moving the region greater than 160 km (99.42 mi) to the southwest. If these range shifts are occurring in birds, then they are likely to be occurring in other taxa as well. One likely result of these shifts is the breakdown of boundaries between biotic provinces, in particular between the Tamaulipan and Austroriparian where the border between the subtropical and temperate zones occurs. The ecological and conservation effects of such a breakdown are likely to be profound.

Birds of South Texas

Rapid range change has been reported for migratory birds in Europe and North America, mostly focused on evidence of northward extension of breeding range boundaries for temperate zone migrants (Matthews et al. 2004; Robinson et al. 2005). South Texas possesses biogeographic attributes that make it especially interesting from the perspective of potential range change. First among these is an extraordinary diversity of plant and animal species unique in North America north of the tropics. Biogeographers have long recognized this attribute, and have also recognized the reason for it, namely the fact that the boundaries between three major biota find their limits in the region: warm desert, subtropical, and temperate, titled respectively "Sonoran," "Neotropical," and "Austroriparian" by Cope (1880). Dice (1943) attempted to provide a more rigorous method for recognizing these kinds of regionally-overlapping distributions of plants and animals that are distinct from neighboring regions. He called these regions "biotic provinces," which he defined as areas, "... characterized by peculiarities of vegetation type, ecological climax, flora, fauna, climate, physiography, and soil." Blair (1950), using this definition, defined seven biotic provinces for Texas: Austroriparian, Tamaulipan, Kansan, Navahonian, Chihuahuan, Texan, and Balconian. Rappole et al. (1994), using animal and plant distributions and climatic parameters, recognized five biotic provinces, dividing Blair's "Balconian Biotic Province" between the Kansan and Austroriparian, and lumping his "Texan Biotic Province" into the Austroriparian, due to their lack of distinctive floral and faunal elements (Figure 1). Four major biotic regions occur in the South Texas region as defined by Norwine and John (Chapter 1, this book): Chihuahuan

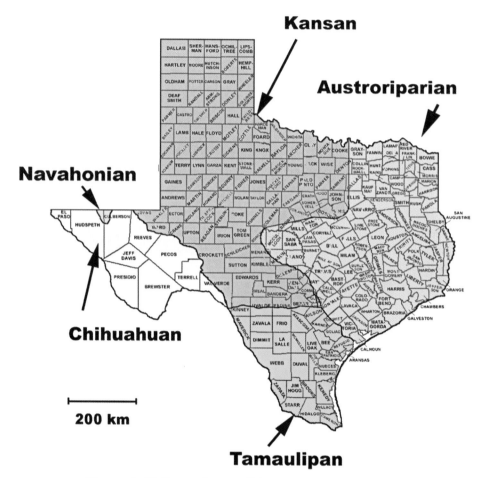

Figure 1. Biotic provinces of Texas.

(warm desert), Kansan (temperate grasslands), Tamaulipan (subtropical), and Austroriparian (south temperate forests). In addition, there is a fifth biotic limit, namely that between the tropics and subtropics, i.e., limit of frost-free climate, located about 300 km (186.41 mi) south of the Texas-Mexico border where the northern end of the Veracruz Biotic Province meets the southern end of the Tamaulipan Biotic Province (Goldman and Moore 1946). As a result of these major biotic boundaries, hundreds of species of animals and plants reach the northern or eastern extent of their ranges in northeastern Mexico or South Texas. The definition of these limits is made relatively clear by the more-or-less regular dissection of the region's coastal plain by rivers, which provide east-west bands of riparian habitat at intervals of 50 to 150 km (24.85 to 93.21 mi) along the north-south shoreline of the Gulf of Mexico. Historically these bands of riparian habitat were separated by large extents of semi-arid thorn scrub, often replaced now by agricultural crops, e.g. cotton and sorghum. The intervening habitats are unsuitable for riparian species, and vice versa for the thorn scrub species, so the search for range limits can be focused on relatively well-defined areas.

A second factor favoring precise definition of species' breeding ranges in the region is the long history of biological investigation, beginning during the Mexican War (1846-1848), and becoming increasingly systematic and extensive up to the present. These factors help to make establishment of the northeastern edge of the breeding range for tropical, subtropical, and warm desert bird species in the South Texas region at least feasible. An additional factor makes possible the documentation of rapid range change, namely the fortuitous publication of three important works summarizing what was known of Texas bird distribution at well-spaced time intervals covering nearly a century of information on Texas bird distribution: Strecker's The Birds of Texas in 1912; Oberholser's The Bird Life of Texas in 1974; and the Texas Ornithological Society's Handbook of Texas Birds (Lockwood and Freeman 2004). In addition to these, Gehlbach et al. (1976) published a worked focused specifically on defining the northern limit of tropical bird distribution in northeastern Mexico.

In this chapter, we examine evidence of avian range change in northeastern Mexico and South Texas, and consider what factors might help to explain range shifts for those species in which they apparently have occurred.

Methods

We use historical literature to document bird species' breeding ranges in northeastern Mexico and Texas during the early, mid-, and late 1900s, and compare these accounts with more recent data reported in the literature, personal communication, or personal observation.

Results

Table 1. Former and current northern and eastern extent of breeding range for subtropical, warm desert, and tropical bird species in Texas and northeastern Mexico. References to biotic provinces are abbreviated as follows: A - Austroriparian; C - Chihuahuan; K - Kansan; T - Tamaulipan; V - Veracruz. See Figure 1 for Texas biotic province and county locations.[1]

Species	Former Extent	Current Extent[1]
Black-bellied Whistling-Duck *Dendrocygna autumnalis*	T - Lower Rio Grande (Cameron, Hidalgo Counties) (1912[2])	K - Tarrant and Dallas Counties. A - Orange County
Masked Duck *Nomonyx dominicus*	T - Occasional on the Lower Rio Grande (Cameron County) (1912)	A - Occasional breeding to Jefferson County
Gambel's Quail *Callipepla gambelii*	C - El Paso County (1912); along the Rio Grande, El Paso, Presidio Counties (1974[3])	C - El Paso, Presidio, Hudspeth, Jeff Davis, and Culberson Counties
Least Grebe *Tachybaptus dominicus*	T - Lower Rio Grande (Cameron and Hidalgo Counties) (1912); Nueces County (1951[4])	A - Harris, Bastrop Counties.; K - Bexar County
Hook-billed Kite *Chondrohierax uncinatus*	V; T - single breeding record (1964) for Hidalgo County (1974)	T - Hidalgo and Starr Counties
Gray Hawk *Buteo nitidus*	T - Occasional along the Rio Grande (Hidalgo County) (1974)	T- Rio Grande (Hidalgo to Webb Counties); rare to casual north to Kleberg County
Short-tailed Hawk *Buteo brachyurus*	V; T - Unrecorded in Texas prior to 1989 when found in Starr County (2004[5])	T - lower Rio Grande Valley
White-tailed Hawk *Buteo albicaudatus*	T - Refugio County (1974)	A - Harris, Galveston Counties
Red-billed Pigeon *Patagioenas flavirostris*	T - Cameron and Hidalgo Counties (1912)	T - Kenedy County (1973[6]).
White-winged Dove *Zenaida asiatica*	T - Bee County (1974).	K - Dallas, Tarrant Counties
White-tipped Dove *Leptotila verreauxi*	T - Cameron and Hidalgo Counties (1912).	T - Refugio County
Green Parakeet *Aratinga holochlora*	V - Rio Corona, Tamaulipas (1976[7]).	T - Cameron, Hidalgo, Starr Counties
Red-crowned Parrot *Amazona virdiginalis*	V - Rio Corona, Tamaulipas) (1976).	T - Cameron, Hidalgo, Starr Counties
Groove-billed Ani *Crotophaga sulcirostris*	T - Nueces County (1957[8]).	A - Gonzales County; K - Bexar County (Mitchell Lake).
Western Screech-Owl *Megascops kennicottii*	C - discovered along the Rio Grande, 1961, Brewster to Val Verde Counties (1974).	K - Kerr County

Table 1 continued.

Species	Former Extent	Current Extent[1]
Ferruginous Pygmy-Owl *Glaucidium brasilianum*	T - Lower Rio Grande Valley; Cameron and Hidalgo Counties (1912)	T - Kenedy County
Lesser Nighthawk *Chordeiles acutipennis*	T- Refugio County (1912)	A- Calhoun County; K - Bexar County
Common Pauraque *Nyctidromus albicollis*	T - Refugio County (1912).	A - Dewitt, Karnes, Victoria and Matagorda Counties
Common Poorwill *Phalaenoptilus nuttallii*	C ; K - eastern portion (Baylor, Stonewall, Young Counties); T - northeast to Refugio County	A - Bastrop County
White-throated Swift *Aeronautes saxatalis*	C - Brewster and Davis Counties (1912, 1974).	C - East to Pecos and Val Verde Counties (1980[9]).
Buff-bellied Hummingbird *Amazilia yucatanensis*	T - Cameron County (1957)	A - Victoria, Matagorda, Karnes, Dewitt Counties
Magnificent Hummingbird *Eugenes fulgens*	C - southern Brewster County (1974).	C - Culberson County
Lucifer Hummingbird *Calothorax lucifer*	C - Southern Brewster, Presidio Counties (1974).	C - Davis County
Black-chinned Hummingbird *Archilochus alexandri*	T - San Patricio County (1974).	T - Goliad, Aransas Counties; A - Dewitt County
Ringed Kingfisher *Ceryle torquata*	T - Starr and Hidalgo Counties (1974).	T - Refugio County; K - Uvalde County; A- Travis County
Green Kingfisher *Chlorceryle americana*	A - north to Mason County, east to Travis County; T - Starr County (1974)·	T - Refugio County; A - Jackson County
Golden-fronted Woodpecker *Melanerpes aurifrons*	T - Refugio County; K - north to Armstrong County, east to Foard County (1974).	K - Clay, Bell Counties; A - Calhoun County
Ladder-backed Woodpecker *Picoides scalaris*	"...west of long. 97□W..." (K - Cooke County; T) (1957)	A- Lavaca, Jackson, Matagorda Counties
Northern Beardless-Tyrannulet *Camptostoma imberbe*	T - Cameron and Hidalgo Counties (1974)	T - Kenedy County
Black Phoebe *Sayornis nigricans*	C; K - east to Tom Green County (1912); T - north and east to Llera, Tamaulipas (1950[9]).	T - Starr, Hidalgo, Live Oak Counties
Say's Phoebe *Sayornis saya*	C - east to Pecos County (1974).	K - Midland, Crocket, Val Verde Counties
Vermilion Flycatcher *Pyrocephalus rubinus*	C; K - north to Midland County; T - northeast to Nueces County (1957, 1974).	K - Jones County; A - Coryell County
Ash-throated Flycatcher *Myiarchus cinerascens*	K - north to Randall County, east to Wilbarger County; T - San Patricio County (1974)	K - throughout Kansan Biotic Province in Texas east to Clay County; T - north and east to Goliad County
Brown-crested Flycatcher *Myiarchus tyrannulus*	T - Hidalgo and Cameron Counties (1957).	A - Dewitt, Victoria Counties

Table 1 continued.

Species	Former Extent	Current Extent[1]
Great Kiskadee *Pitangus sulphuratus*	T - Nueces County (1957).	A - Dewitt, Karnes, Calhoun Counties
Tropical Kingbird *Tyrannus melancholichus*	V - Rio Corona, Tamaulipas	T - Lower Rio Grande
Couch's Kingbird *Tyrannus couchii*	T - Hidalgo, Cameron Counties (1957).	A - Calhoun County ; K - Bexar County; A - Travis County
Gray Vireo *Vireo vicinior*	C - east to Brewster and Davis Counties (1974).	K - north to Tom Green County, east to Real County
Hutton's Vireo *Vireo huttoni*	C - east to Brewster and Davis Counties	K - east to Real, Uvalde, Bexar Counties
Yellow-green Vireo *Vireo flavoviridis*	V - Rio Corona, Tamaulipas (1957)	T - Cameron, Hidalgo Counties
Green Jay *Cyanocorax yncas*	T - Webb, Starr, Hidalgo, Cameron Counties (1957)	T - Karnes, Dewitt, Goliad Counties
Western Scrub-Jay *Aphelocoma californica*	C; K - Kerr, Concho Counties (1912).	K - Cottle County; A - Bell, Williamson, Travis Counties
Tamaulipas Crow *Corvus imparatus*	T - Magiscatzin, Tamaulipas (1950[8]).	T - Cameron County
Chihuahuan Raven *Corvus cryptoleucus*	C; K - Wichita County; T - northeast to Starr County (1912)	T - Kenedy County
Common Raven *Corvus corax*	C; A - Llano County (1974).	A - Williamson and Travis Counties
Cave Swallow *Petrochelidon fulva*	C; K - Edwards, Kerr Counties (1957).	K - Hopkins County; A - Jefferson County
Black-crested Titmouse *Baeolophus atricristatus*	C; T; K - north and east to Bosque County (1974).	K - Montague County
Verdin *Auriparus flaviceps*	C; K; T (1974)	K - Baylor County.; A - Bell, Calhoun Counties
Bushtit *Psaltriparus minimus*	C - Davis, Brewster Counties (1912).	A - Williamson, Comal Counties; K - Randall County, .
Cactus Wren *Campylorhynchus brunneicapillus*	C; K - Bexar County; T - lower Rio Grande Valley (1912).	K - Floyd County; A - Bell, Williamson Counties; T - Refugio County
Black-tailed Gnatcatcher *Polioptila melanura*	C; T - Hidlago, Cameron Counties (1974).	K - Uvalde; T - Frio, Duval Counties
Clay-colored Robin *Turdus grayi*	V - Rio Corona, Tamaulipas (1976).	T - Hidalgo, Cameron Counties; A - Gonzales County?
Long-billed Thrasher *Toxostoma longirostre*	T - Nueces County (1957).	A - Calhoun County; K - Bexar County

Table 1 continued.

Species	Former Extent	Current Extent[1]
Curve-billed Thrasher *Toxostoma curvirostre*	C; K - Kent, Sutton Counties; T (1974)	K - Lipscomb, Wichita Counties; A - Williamson County
Crissal Thrasher *Toxostoma crissale*	C - Brewster County	K - Howard, Crockett Counties
Tropical Parula *Parula pitiayumi*	T - Starr, Hidalgo, Cameron Counties (1957).	T - Nueces County; A - Calhoun, Victoria Counties; C - Jeff Davis County; K - Val Verde County
Yellow Warbler (Mangrove Warbler race) *Dendroica petechia erithachorides*	V - southern Tamaulipas (1998[10]).	T - Cameron County (South Padre Island).
Olive Sparrow *Arremonops rufivirgatus*	T - San Patricio County (1912).	A - Calhoun (1983[11]), Dewitt, Karnes Counties
Canyon Towhee *Pipilo fuscus*	C; K- Tom Green County (1912).	K - Randall County; A - Williamson County
Botteri's Sparrow *Aimophila botterii*	T - Lower Rio Grande Valley (1912).	T - San Patricio County (1983).
Rufous-crowned Sparrow *Aimophila ruficeps*	C; K - few localities north to Grayson County (1974).	K - most of province in state north to Lipscomb County
Black-throated Sparrow *Amphispiza bilineata*	T - Aransas County (1957).	T - Bee County
Pyrrhuloxia *Cardinalis sinuata*	C; T - largely absent (1912); K - southern portion (1974).	K - Howard County; A - Calhoun County
Varied Bunting *Passerina versicolor*	T - Cameron, Hidalgo Counties (1912).	C - along the Rio Grande Plain; K - Kimble County; T - Zapata, Starr Counties
Bronzed Cowbird *Molothrus aeneus*	T - north to Bexar County (1912).	C; K - Bosque County; A - Matagorda County
Hooded Oriole *Icterus cucullatus*	T - Cameron and Hidalgo Counties (1912).	T - Nueces County
Altamira Oriole *Icterus gularis*	No Texas records (1912)	T - Zapata, Starr, Hidalgo, Cameron Counties
Audubon's Oriole *Icterus graduacauda*	T - Starr, Hidalgo, Cameron Counties (1957).	T - Goliad County
Scott's Oriole *Icterus parisorum*	C (1912)	K - Coke County; A - Travis County
Lesser Goldfinch *Carduelis psaltria*	C; K - Midland County; A - Bell County; T - Bee County	K - Wheeler County; Wichita County; A - Coryell, Dewitt Counties.; T - Goliad, Nueces Counties

[1] Based on Lockwood and Freeman (2004) supplemented by information from W. Sekula unless otherwise stated.
[2] Strecker (1912).
[3] Oberholser (1974).
[4] Packard (1951)

[5] Lockwood and Freeman (2004)
[6] Fall (1973).
[7] Gehlbach et al. (1976).
[8] AOU (1957).
[9] Friedman et al. (1950).
[10] AOU (1998)

The information summarized in Table 1 indicates that breeding ranges for seventy species that reach the northern and/or eastern edge of their breeding range in Texas have undergone northward and/or eastward shifts. These shifts appear to have occurred over the past century, but the pace of change seems to have accelerated, and many of these species have shown significant changes within the past thirty years. The changes in range are quite variable among species, ranging from a few km for birds like the Golden-fronted Woodpecker (*Melanerpes aurifrons*) and Black-crested Titmouse (*Baeolophus atricristatus*) to hundreds of km for the White-winged Dove (*Zenaida asiatica*) and Cave Swallow (*Petrochelidon fulva*).

These range changes fall into three major categories:

1) subtropical species whose ranges have expanded northward and/or eastward within the South Texan subtropical zone (Tamaulipan Biotic Province) or beyond it into the temperate zone (Austroriparian Biotic Province);

2) tropical species whose ranges have expanded from the limit of the tropics defined by Gehlbach et al. (1976) at the Rio Corona (a tributary of the Rio Soto La Marina) northward 300 km in the subtropics to South Texas (the lower Rio Grande); and

3) warm desert species whose ranges have expanded northward and/or eastward into southern, central, or even eastern Texas.

An example of a species whose range evidently has shifted northward within the subtropics is the Green Jay (*Cyanocorax yncas*) (Figure 2). Strecker (1912) reported its range as restricted to the Rio Grande Valley (Laredo to Brownsville); Rappole and Blacklock (1985) reported its range as extending north into southern Nueces County. At present (March, 2007), there are apparently resident populations on the Welder Wildlife Refuge along the Aransas River, which forms the border between San Patricio and Refugio counties (JHR, personal observation). According to refuge personnel, these birds have been present on the refuge for at least the past four years (T. Blankenship, S. Glasscock, L. Drawe personal communication).

The Green Parakeet (*Aratinga holochlora*) is a tropical species listed by Gehlbach et al. (1976) as reaching its northern limit along the Rio Corona. The breeding range for this bird now appears to have shifted northward in riparian and residential areas to include the lower Rio Grande (Lockwood and Freeman 2004) (Figure 3).

The Black-tailed Gnatcatcher (*Polioptila melanura*) is representative of those warm desert species whose populations appear to have shifted northward and eastward over the past century. Strecker (1912) reported the bird, eastern populations of which were then recognized as a separate species, the Plumbeous Gnatcatcher (*Polioptila plumbea*), as an, "Abundant summer resident of the high mountains of the trans-Pecos region, east during the migrations to Rio Grande City." Oberholser (1974) shows the bird as at least present in summer along the lower Rio Grande; Lockwood and Freeman (2004) show the bird as a breeding resident along the entire Rio Grande as well as northward beyond the Rio Grande Plain (Figure 4).

Discussion

Evidence indicating the presence of breeding populations for tropical, subtropical, and warm desert species north and/or east of their historical range has become increasingly common in recent years, as documented in Table 1 of this paper and Figures 2 to 4. For the most part, such range extensions have been attributed to increased number, vigilance, access, or expertise of field investigators. For instance, Fall (1973) in his report on northward range extensions for ten subtropical species in South Texas stated that the area in Kenedy County where his observations were made, "... is inaccessible to the public and as a result has been virtually excluded from both past and present ornithological investigation." These explanations now seem inadequate based on the number of species involved and degree of change.

Unfortunately, in most cases, range change information is based solely on observation of individuals in the appropriate habitat and time period. Actual confirmation of breeding (nest, eggs, recently-fledged young) within the new range is mostly lacking. Thus, the information is indicative but not yet conclusive evidence of significant and pervasive northward and eastward range shift for a large suite of desert, subtropical, and tropical species.

In some cases, there are species-specific explanations for these shifts. For instance, the recent appearance of tropical psittacids like the Green Parakeet along the lower Rio Grande is often credited to establishment of breeding populations among escaped cage birds (Lockwood and Freeman 2004). Similarly, some authors have attributed the large northward range shift of the White-winged Dove (hundreds of km) to extensive supplemental food now available in Texas cities (Small et al. 2005), and Cave Swallow range expansion has been related to newly available "man made structures" (Lockwood and Freeman 2004). However, for the majority of species, there is no obvious explanation of this sort. In fact, habitat change, which is the usual explanation for changes in breeding bird distribution, would appear to favor contraction of the South Texas breeding range for many species rather than expansion. For instance, in the lower Rio Grande Valley less than 5% of native thorn forest and riparian habitat remain (Purdy 1983).

The fact that ranges for seventy South Texas species appear to have expanded northward and/or eastward during a period when habitat for many of them was declining in the areas into which they were expanding indicates the possibility that range change was favored by some pervasive environmental factor. We suggest that climate change, and specifically increasing mean annual temperatures, could be that factor. South Texas climate is subject to radical short- and long- term fluctuation (Norwine et al. Chapter 2, this book). Thus, it is notoriously difficult to determine trends over a period as short as thirty years. Keeping this caveat in mind, mean annual temperature in South Texas has shown a marked increase over the past three decades, in line with warming trends elsewhere (Norwine et al. Chapter 2, this volume). We suggest that northward

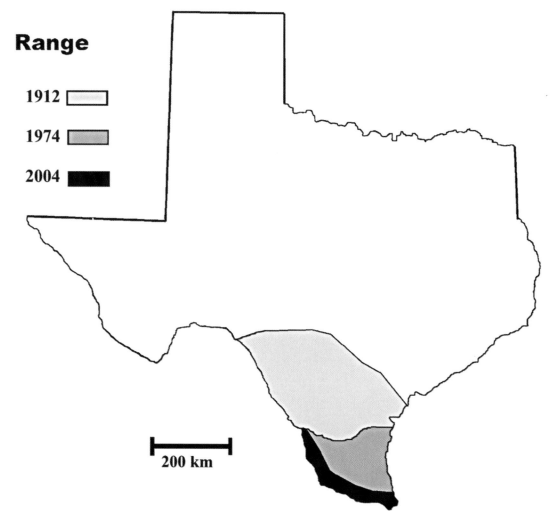

Figure 2. Green Jay range change in Texas, 1912 to 2004

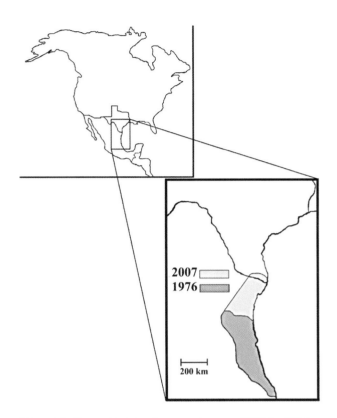

Figure 3. Green Parakeet range change, 1976 to 2004

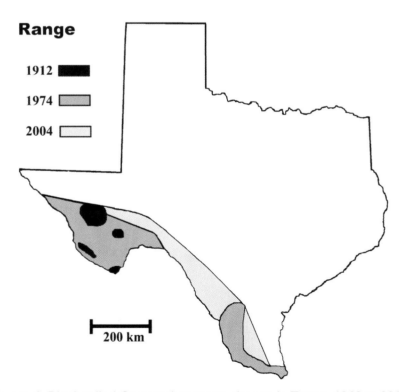

Figure 4. Black-tailed Gnatcatcher range change in Texas, 1912 to 2004

range expansion of subtropical bird species in South Texas may be related in ways that are not yet understood to increasing temperature. In any event, we are not aware of any other single environmental factor with which range change for seventy bird species might be correlated.

If our hypothesis is correct, the ecological and evolutionary effects could be profound. Birds are certainly among the most visible parts of the region's biota, as well as being among the most mobile. Nevertheless, if bird ranges are changing, it seems likely that ranges for members of many other groups of both plants and animals also are changing, and probably at rates similar to those of birds in many cases. If this kind of change is occurring across phyla, then major shifts in the boundaries of biomes may be underway.

The evolutionary consequences of biome boundary shifts should be evident quite quickly, especially along the border between the Tamaulipan Biotic Province and the Austroriparian Biotic Province, which is generally sited at the San Antonio River in the Texas coastal plain where the river constitutes the border between Refugio and Calhoun counties (Rappole et al. 1994). Many closely-related taxa of animals and plants reach their range boundaries here, with the temperate representative of super-species complexes reaching the southern terminus of their range and subtropical representatives reaching the northern terminus: for instance, the Black-crested Titmouse (subtropical) and Tufted Titmouse (*Baeolophus bicolor*) (temperate); Florida Woodrat (*Neotoma floridana*) (temperate) and Mexican Woodrat (*N. mexicana*) (subtropical); Black-spotted Newt (*Notophthalmus meridionalis*) (subtropical) and Red-spotted Newt (*N. viridescens*) (temperate) , to mention just a few (Blair 1950; Rappole et al. 1994).

Conclusions

Based on the observational data summarized in this paper, we state the following hypothesis: Rapid (i.e., measured in years rather than decades or centuries) northward and eastward shift in the breeding ranges of several tropical, subtropical, and warm desert bird species in South Texas and northeastern Mexico is occurring due to climatic change. At present, the data necessary to test this hypothesis are largely lacking. Most of the evidence for this change is in the form of reports by untrained observers to the Texas Ornithological Society of birds being seen regularly in places where they were not previously known. Clearly, a concerted effort must be made to test this hypothesis.

If our hypothesis is correct, we make the following predictions, all of which are readily amenable to field and/or laboratory tests:

1) Rapid shifts in subtropical, semi-arid, and warm desert bird species' breeding ranges will continue to occur across the Texas region and beyond: largely northward and eastward of the historical range.

2) Evidence of northward and eastward shift of breeding range will accumulate for many additional bird species in Texas whose currently-known range limit is located well south or west of the region.

3) Evidence of northward and eastward range shifts will accumulate for all other aspects of the region's biota, in addition to birds.

4) Northward and eastward shift of some species native to the Tamaulipan Biotic Province, i.e., those with closely-related congeners in the Austroriparian Biotic Province (e.g. *Baeolophus atricristatus* and *B. bicolor*), will lead to rapid increase in genetic mixing between the two populations.

5) Borders between biotic provinces, biomes, and similar biogeographically-defined regional entities will not simply shift. They will break down.

Norwine and John (Preface, this volume) state in reference to the likely future effects of climate change in eastern South Texas, "Imagine picking up the entire region and moving it (a) one hundred or so miles (161 km) west (i.e., toward the Chihuahuan Desert) and (b) a similar distance south." Based on the observed shifts in bird species' distribution summarized here, it would appear that these changes are well underway. They are likely to have profound consequences for the biota.

Acknowledgments

The following individuals provided information on current ranges for one or more species discussed in this chapter: W. Sekula, D. Muschalek, T. Blankenship, S. Glasscock, and L. Drawe. JHR thanks the Smithsonian National Zoological Park, in particular J. Seidensticker and S. Monfort, for authorizing sabbatical leave to conduct this research, and the Welder Wildlife Foundation, in particular L. Drawe, for serving as the Texas host institution during that leave.

Literature Cited

American Ornithologists' Union. 1957. *The A. O. U. Check-list of North American Birds* 5th ed. Baltimore, MD: American Ornithologists' Union.

American Ornithologists' Union. 1983. *The A. O. U. Check-list of North American Birds* 6th ed. Baltimore, MD: American Ornithologists' Union.

American Ornithologists' Union.1998. *The A. O. U. check-list of North American Birds* 7th ed. Baltimore, MD: American Ornithologists' Union.

Blair, W. F. 1950. The Biotic Provinces of Texas. *Texas Journal of Science* 2:93-117.

Cope, E. D. 1880. On the Zoological Position of Texas. *Bulletin of the U. S. National Museum* 17:1-51.

Dice, L. R. 1943. *The Biotic Provinces of North America* Ann Arbor, MI: University of Michigan Press.

Fall, B. A. 1973. Noteworthy Bird Records from South Texas (Kenedy County). *Southwestern Naturalist* 18:244-247.

Friedman, H., L. Griscom, and R. T. Moore. 1950. Distributional Checklist of the Birds of Mexico Part 1. *Cooper Ornithological Club, Pacific Coast Avifauna* 29:1-436.

Gehlbach, F. R., D. O. Dillon, H. L. Harrell, S. E. Kennedy, and K. R. Wilson. 1976. *Avifauna of the Rio Corona, Tamaulipas, Mexico: Northeastern Limit of the Tropics.* Auk 93:53-65.

Goldman, E. A., and R. T. Moore. 1946. The Biotic Provinces of Mexico. *Journal of Mammalogy* 26:347-360.

Lasley, G. W., and J. P. Gee, 1991. The First Nesting Record of the Hutton's Vireo (*Vireo huttoni*) East of the Pecos River, Texas. *Bulletin of the Texas Ornithological Society* 24:23-24.

Lockwood, M. W., 2001. Birds of the Texas hill country. University of Texas Press, Austin, Texas.

Lockwood, M. W. and B. Freeman. 2004. *The Texas Ornithological Society Handbook of Texas Birds.* College Station, TX: Texas A&M University Press.

Matthews, S. N., R. J. O'Connor, L. R. Iverson, and A. M. Prasad. 2004. *Atlas of Climate Change Effects in 150 Bird Species of the Eastern United States* Delaware, OH: U.S. Department of Agriculture, Forest Service.

Maxwell, T. C. 1980. Significant Nesting Records of Birds from Western Texas. *Bulletin of the Texas Ornithological Society* 13:2-6.

Oberholser, H. C. 1974. *The Bird Life of Texas* Austin, TX: University of Texas Press.

Packard, F. M. 1951. *Birds of the Central Coast of Texas.* Unpublished Manuscript, Archives, Sinton, TX: Welder Wildlife Foundation.

Purdy, P. C. 1983. *Agricultural, Industrial, and Urban Development in Relation to the Eastern White-winged Dove.* M. S. Thesis, Colorado State University, Fort Collins, Colorado.

Peterson, J. J., and B. R. Zimmer 1998. *Birds of the Trans Pecos* Austin, TX: University of Texas Press.

Rappole, J. H., and G. W. Blacklock. 1985. *Birds of the Texas Coastal Bend* College Station, TX: Texas A&M University Press.

Rappole, J. H., T. Fulbright, J. Norwine, and R. Bingham. 1994. The Forest-Grassland Boundary in Texas: Population Differentiation without Geographic Isolation. *Proceedings of the Third International Rangelands Congress* Panjab Singh ed. Jhansi, India: Range Management Society of India p. 167-177.

Robinson, R. A., J. A. Learmonth, A. M. Hutson, C. D. Macleod, T. H. Sparks, D. I. Leech, G. J. Pierce, M. M. Rehfisch, and H. Q. P. Crick. 2005. Climate Change and Migratory Species. *British Trust for Ornithology Report #414*, Thetford, England: British Trust for Ornithology.

Small, M. F., C. L. Schaefer, J. T. Baccus, and J. A. Roberson, 2005. Breeding Ecology of White-winged Doves in a Recently Colonized Urban Environment. *Wilson Bulletin* 117:172-176.

Strecker, J. K., Jr. 1912. The Birds of Texas. *Baylor University Bulletin* 15:1-69.

9

South Texas Climate 2100:
Reflections, Prospects, Prescriptions

Robert Harriss

"In this world nothing is certain except death and taxes." Ben Franklin (attributed)

Doomsday Reconsidered

In January 2007, the *Bulletin of the Atomic Scientists* advanced the "Doomsday Clock" on its cover from seven to five minutes to midnight, noting "the deteriorating state of global affairs*."* The increased accessibility of nuclear weapons to desperate and irresponsible people, emerging biotechnologies and nanotechnologies that have highly uncertain benefits and costs, and the scientific consensus that global warming could lead to intolerable impacts on human well-being are noted with great concern in essays by highly respected experts in science, engineering, and public policy. The common theme across these essays was that future generations will be living in an increasingly complicated and more perilous world.

On the other hand, other respected scholars see ample cause for optimism about the future. As Flynn (2007) states, "Building a resilient society in not about caving in to our fears. Instead, it is about inventorying what is truly precious and ensuring its durability so that we can remain true to our ideals no matter what tempest the future may bring." Human societies, writ large, have exhibited remarkable resilience at the edge of disaster, exhibiting considerable capacity for coping with changing environments and threats to survival. In this chapter, we highlight some of the ingredients that might imbue us with the sense of local and regional purpose necessary to creating more adaptive, resilient, and sustainable futures for people and nature in South Texas.

Creating Adaptive, Resilient, and Sustainable Futures in South Texas

"The flight into tradition, out of a combination of humility and presumption, can bring about nothing in itself other than self deception and blindness in relation to the historical moment." M. Heidegger

The previous chapters of this book have provided a scientific and engineering assessment of possible environmental impacts and consequences of the projected twenty-first century global warming likely to emerge across our South Texas landscape. There is little doubt that our current "problem climate" may become evermore problematic as a result of environmental changes described in the scenarios discussed in this book. If present and future generations of South Texan's are to avoid the most serious threats posed by global warming and influence the future for the better, we need to have understandable and justifiable stories of where we may be headed and how we might change course. The art and science of building a more adaptive, resilient, and sustainable South Texas future will be, in most instances, best understood in our particular local and regional, social, and ecological contexts; where complexity is comprehensible; where consensus is most likely; and where most decisions relevant to our region will originate.

While there are well described examples of past societies that collapsed due to a lack of capacity for adapting to environmental change (Diamond 2005), humanity has also demonstrated an amazing range of adaptations that enabled expansion to every continent except Antarctica. For the current circumstances and global warming impact scenarios discussed in this book, we conclude that adaptive strategies that enhance resilience and sustainability are urgently needed to cope with the threats of both current weather extremes and the projected global warming scenarios. Our strategy has three areas of focus:

1) protecting our most vulnerable people;
2) protecting unique public and cultural resources; and
3) insuring policy integration at the regional scale where social, economic, political, and environmental connections and coordination are most essential to making progress towards more adaptive, resilient, and sustainable futures.

Steps to a More Adaptive, Resilient, and Sustainable South Texas

"Will transformation. O be inspired for the flame in which a thing eludes you, resplendent with change. For the spirit of creativity, which masters what is earthly, loves in the figure's swing nothing more than the turning point."
Rainer Maria Rilke

The previous chapters of this book have focused specifically on how global warming will grow in importance as a threat to the existence of our coastal and interior ecosystems and to the water resources that are crucial to the sustainability of our communities and commerce in South Texas. The past history of weather and climate impacts on loss of lives and property supports our notion that Texans are seldom adequately resilient or adaptive to occurrences of severe drought, flooding, windstorms, heat waves, and other hazardous weather and climate events (Bomar 1983). In fact, the entire State of Texas has a long record of leading the nation in disaster losses, presidential disaster declarations, and other metrics used to measure societal vulnerability to impacts of weather and climate (e.g., Cutter 2001, 2006; Social Vulnerability Index for the United States 2007).

The aftermath of the devastation wrought by Hurricane's Katrina and Rita on the coasts of Texas, Louisiana, and Mississippi pointed to the familiar characteristics that lead to catastrophic disasters. First, coastal and floodplain landscapes are being developed in a manner that increasingly places more lives and property at risk to threats from hurricanes, floods, droughts, and other environmental hazards. For example, unfettered growth in South Texas and adjacent areas of Northern Mexico is increasing the number of people and value of property at risk to threats of hurricanes, storm surge, flooding, water shortages, sea level rise, and other related weather and climate hazards described in the previous chapters of this book. Second, natural ecosystems and physical infrastructures that are crucial to community resilience and quality of life are deteriorating. The Texas Section of the American Society of Civil Engineers has detailed the serious nature of degraded and failing bridges, dams, roads, and other infrastructure throughout the state, including South Texas (TS-ASCE 2004). Third, Hurricane Katrina demonstrated that we have been unwilling at all levels of government to invest in the people and organizational capabilities necessary to mitigate or adapt to the impacts associated with extreme weather and climate events. Fourth, one of the lessons learned from previous disasters in South Texas, and elsewhere, is that within months, after the media attention goes away, we go back to business as usual. We can see all of these factors at work everyday in South Texas, and in our neighboring communities across the Texas-Mexico border.

Common sense suggests that reducing social and economic vulnerabilities to known risks is an obvious first step to becoming more resilient to future threats posed by the potential impacts of global warming discussed in this book. Poverty, unhealthy living and working conditions, limited access to education and other public services, and related factors are common in the rapidly growing low income segment of the population in South Texas and adjacent areas of Northern Mexico (Murdoch 2003). The unincorporated South Texas "colonias" may be among the most vulnerable communities in America. Some of the most serious elements of the social vulnerability in these communities have been discussed by Ward (1999).

First steps in a transition to safer and more sustainable South Texas communities will require attention to:

1) the **sensitivities** of people and ecosystems to environmental change with special attention to hazards posed by extreme weather and climate events,

2) human and ecosystem **adaptability**, which is the coping capacity of people and landscapes mitigate or adjust to weather and climate hazards, and

3) the **causal factors** that underlie the social vulnerabilities to disaster.

The findings of this book suggest some urgent next steps:

1) conducting a comprehensive study of trends and indicators of disaster resistance and resilience to impacts of weather and climate extremes in South Texas and bordering towns in Mexico, and documenting progress, if any, made towards becoming more a more resilient society,

2) a vulnerability mapping program to guide immediate actions that will enhance the resilience and sustainability of our most vulnerable citizens and vital ecosystems, and

3) the engagement of our college youth, the next-generation citizens and community leaders of our region, in the design of a long-term sustainability action plan and policy recommendations for implementation.

Previous studies that provide both important insights and integrative methodologies relevant to conducting a socioeconomic assessment include Mazarr (1999), Murdoch et al. (2003), and Sharp (1998) Sharp (1994) and Schmandt et al. (2000). Cash et al. (2006) document the importance of paying close attention to scale and cross-scale dynamics as they influence governance and information relevant to planning for resilience and sustainability. The U.S.-Mexico border may be the most challenging place in North America to enhance resilience and sustainability due to a long history of benign neglect of a plethora of issues related to extreme poverty, poor quality education, and other social and health issues. The width of the Rio Grande, which can shrink physically to scores of yards in some places, might well seem more like hundreds of kilometers politically. Indeed, in some cases, even coordination of activities on just one side of the border is often difficult or nonexistent. In the end, human ties are split by national, state, and local government boundaries. Some commendable efforts to overcome the political boundaries can be seen and applauded, but coordinated regional decision-making about regional problems remains the exception and not the rule (Sharp, 1998).

A historical record documenting the social, economic, political, and environmental evolution of the region and the sectoral impacts and societal/institutional responses to past extreme weather and climate hazards would be important elements for integrating lessons learned about needed coping capacity across the region. Reminding community participants of past experiences with weather and climate disasters is an effective way to gaining their participation in thinking about scenarios of future impacts of climate and weather extremes. Using a forecasting by analogy method, the historical assessment should seek to answer the following questions: How have various segments of each community (schools, industry, residence, etc) adapted (or maladapted) historically to extreme weather and climate events? What lessons, if any, have been learned? What mechanisms of mitigation and/or adaptive response can one design to reduce impacts of future weather and climate events based upon historical experiences? A retrospective analysis is also useful for assessing strategic, legal, and institutional actions that could be crucial to enhancing resilience and sustainability of the South Texas region.[1]

A social assessment should map patterns of human vulnerability according to residential settlement location, socioeconomic stratification, population migration, and key health indicators and other variables. The social analysis should also involve a longitudinal assessment of population distribution and residential settlement, regional migration patterns (seasonal and inter-annual), and urban and rural growth trends and dynamics. Several key questions to be addressed include: What are the underlying causal factors contributing to socioeconomic vulnerability to extreme weather conditions and climate events?[2] What is the differential nature of social vulnerability within and between communities? What segments of society,[3] are more vulnerable to weather and

---

[1] e.g., land use planning, building codes, insurance, community education, etc
[2] income, ethnicity, education, residential location, information access
[3] socioeconomic status, ethnicity, age, gender, education

climate hazards than others? What is the potential for disease outbreak and transmission following events like flooding or extreme heat waves, and what are the homeland security implications for our nation? What are the potential areas of conflict that may arise between the US and Mexican governments or commercial interests as the risk of an extreme weather event increases due to global warming? What are the implications of potential changes in access to land and water among competing interest groups[§] during extreme drought conditions that may accompany global warming?

The Need for a Focus on the Future

"We walk backwards into the future, our eyes fixed on the past."   *Maori proverb*

Learning from the history of how South Texan's have responded to and recovered from past destructive weather and climate events is only one aspect of preparing to be more adaptive, resilient, and sustainable in the coming era of global warming. Forces of social, institutional, political, and technological change will reshape society as the impacts of global warming reshape the environment in which we live. Sustaining a prosperous trajectory for future generations will also require:

1) a transition from the current complex and fragmented decision making processes to an integrative regional approach for natural resource and disaster management;

2) a much more effective engagement of citizens, and especially youth, in the processes of governance; and

3) new metaphors and stories that can stimulate broader public interest in thinking about the long-term sustainability of South Texas and neighboring communities in Mexico.

Cultivating these new foundations of thinking for future generations will require a fundamental restructuring of our educational systems in a manner that inspires confidence in youth that they can successfully solve the challenges of creating better futures. Gardner (2006) has made a compelling case that people will need five cognitive abilities to cope with the complexities of the future—mastery of at least one professional craft; the ability to integrate ideas from different disciplines into a coherent whole and to communicate that integration to others; the capacity to uncover and clarify new problems and phenomena; an awareness of and appreciation for differences among people; and an ethic of one's responsibility as a worker and citizen. Future citizens with these skills will be prepared to consider a paradigm shift in how our region is viewed, focusing on balance, interdependence, and interactivity within a sustainable whole. Changing our ways of thinking, learning, and decision making is difficult, unsettling, and may require a major change in political power structures. The proposed transformations in our systems of education and governance may happen through reflective analysis of the unsustainable nature of our current lifestyles and environmental trends, or be forced on our region by a crisis that creates a sense of urgency and awareness of the need for fundamental change. One certain conclusion from our assessment is that a "business as usual" approach to the future will endanger the livelihoods and lives of all twenty-first century South Texans.

Why, if preventive measures already exist that would better prepare us both for the next hurricane landfall and for future impacts global warming, has our nation, state, and region not adopted them? What are the obstacles that prevent us from be better prepared and more resilient to the threats posed by extreme weather and global warming? How can we improve our capacity for taking prospective actions on becoming more adaptive and resilient to extreme weather and climate? The answer to these questions may lie, at least partially, in the "soft" nature of the fundamental forces that often influence the attention given to social vulnerability: human needs and values, cultures, political and economic power structures, and access to knowledge. Information on these variables is difficult to collect, interpret, and find consensus on. The science and engineering analysis of climate impact analysis is much more robust than the "art" of enhancing the future resilience and sustainability of the South Texas region. We recognize that the art of sustaining our South Texas region will require a clarion call based on an understanding of what drives motivation, aspiration, and will among our citizens and decision makers. It will value the diverse people

---

[§] commercial, environmental, agricultural, maritime, recreation

and cultures of our region and neighboring regions. It will recognize the power of intangibles like history, identity, desire, and their influence on perceptions of what is most important.

The authors of this book cannot predict exactly how global warming will change human lives and landscapes in South Texas during this century. However, this impact assessment does provide a range of plausible information on the trends, extremes, and consequences that may be associated with global warming. Because scenarios of the future do become more uncertain the further into the future the prediction, the state of our understanding must be revisited every five to ten years. As the power of computers increases, our understanding of how changes in human activities and ecosystems influence each other through "feedback" processes will improve and our capabilities for prediction will become more robust.

Measuring Progress

"Without contraries is no progression." William Blake

South Texas is currently a catastrophe waiting to happen. We know that hurricanes, droughts, heat waves, sea level rise, and other weather and climate extremes will intersect with our social vulnerability and fragile ecologies to create future megadisasters. Sadly, leaders and institutions at all levels of governance are underestimating the growing fragility of our region and failing to tap known strategies for enhancing regional resilience and sustainability. Creating a safer and more sustainable future for South Texas is something citizens, the business community, and our elected officials must embrace. It is time to negotiate our fears, mediate what sustainability means to each of us, and to begin organizing for better futures. As Marcel Proust wrote, "The real voyage of discovery consists not in seeking new lands, but in seeking with new eyes." The first step to creating more sustainable futures for South Texas is changing minds, not making more plans.

Progress on achieving a more resilient and sustainable South Texas economy and ecology will occur in small steps. Significant progress on creating a more resilient and sustainable South Texas will require:

- enhancing the safety and resilience of our most vulnerable people in South Texas and adjacent cross-border communities;
- maintaining and enhancing community prosperity and economic resilience in the face of global warming and other threats to sustainable development;
- conserving and giving value to natural ecosystems and cultural heritage; and
- achieving progress on the design and implementation of effective regional policies and financial initiatives dedicated to sustainable development.

Literature Cited

Bomar, G.W. 1983. *Texas Weather* Austin, TX: University of Texas Press.

Cash, D., W.N. Adger, F. Berkes, P. Garden, L. Lebel, P. Olsen, L. Prichard, and O. Young. 2006. Scale and Cross-scale Dynamics: Governance and Information in a Multi-level World, *Ecology and Society* 11(2): article 8, www.ecologyandsociety.org.

Cutter, S. L. ed. 2001. *American Hazardscapes: The Regionalization of Hazards and Disasters* Washington DC: Joseph Henry Press.

Cutter, S. L. 2006. *Hazards, Vulnerability and Environmental Justice* London: Earthscan Publications Ltd.

Cutter S. L. B. J. Boruff, and W. L. Shirley. 2003. *Social Science Quarterly* 84(2):242-261.

Diamond, J. 2005. *Collapse: How Societies Choose to Fail or Succeed* Penguin Group, www.penguin.com.

Gardner, H. 2006. *Five Minds for the Future* Harvard Business School Press, Boston, MA.

Mazarr, M. J. 1999. *Mexico 2005: The Challenges of the New Millennium* Washington, DC: CSIS Press, www.csis.org,

Murdoch, S.H., S. White, Md. Nazrul Hoque, B. Pecotte, X. You, and J. Balkin. 2003. *The New Texas Challenge: Population Change and the Future of Texas* College Station, TX: Texas A&M University Press.

Sharp, J. 1994. *Forces of Change: Shaping the Future of Texas* Austin, TX: Texas Comptroller of Public Accounts,

Sharp, J. 1998. *Bordering the Future: Challenges and Opportunity in the Texas Border Region* Publication #96-599 Austin, TX: Texas Comptroller of Public Accounts.

Schmandt, Jurgen; Ismael Aguilar-Barajas, Mitchell Mathis, Neal Armstrong, Liliana Chapa-Alemán, Salvador Contreras-Balderas, Robert Edwards, María Elena García-Ramirez, Jared Hazleton, María de Lourdes Lozano-Vilano, José de Jesus Navar-Chaidez, Enrique Vogel, and George Ward,. *Water and Sustainable Development in the Binational Lower Rio Grande/Río Bravo Basin.* Final Report to EPA/NSF Water and Watersheds grant program (Grant No. R 824799-01-0), The Woodlands, TX: Houston Advanced Research Center, Center for Global Studies, March 31, 2000.

Social Vulnerability Index for the United States. 2007. accessed on the Internet at: http://www.cas.sc.edu/geog/hrl/sovi.html, May 19, 2007.

Ward, P. M. 1999. *Colonias and Public Policy in Texas and Mexico: Urbanization by Stealth*, Austin, TX: University of Texas Press.

Epilogue

Letter to a Young Reader

Kuruvilla John and Jim Norwine

Things change.
Not all change is benign or beneficial: much is "bad".
Bad change can be endured, even made "good".
If.

Dear Reader: By now you know that you hold in your hand a "global warming" book mostly lacking in policies or prescriptions. There is a place for advocacy but this is not that place. The singular reason-to-be of *The Changing Climate of South Texas 1900 to 2100* was to provide citizens and leaders with <u>knowledge</u>; knowledge in the form of a readable, state-of-the-science assessment of what we know and where we are headed. We hope you agree that, although this volume lacks elements we wish could have included such the social implications of our current climate scenarios, an important and urgent purpose has been accomplished.

The Changing Climate of South Texas 1900 to 2100 was the work of leading scholarly authorities, to whom we are deeply grateful. As you have read their chapters, you have found that they explained that the existing semi-arid, subtropical climate, which is already "problematic," is very likely to become considerably more so by the end of this century. In 2100, South Texas will be warmer, perhaps very much warmer. It will probably be more moisture-variable, with both more intense storms and more and longer droughts. Paradoxically it may be both rainier as a consequence of influences such as heightened El Ninos and/or tropical disturbances, and yet also drier in terms of average soil moisture due to increased evaporation rates. The potential magnitude and shock of this change was illustrated in Chapter Two with an idea that at first blush seems hyperbolic: "Imagine Corpus Christi moved to Laredo by the year 2100." In fact, while that prospect might prove an exaggeration in one sense - one hundred years may not be long enough to shift the climate of Corpus Christi from subhumid to semi-desert - it is probably too moderate in other ways. After all, Laredo will not have to deal with the very real threat of sea-level rise.

Our expert contributors have also shown that the potential regional impacts and implications of such changes will, with exceptions, tend to be unfavorable for most natural and human economies and ecologies. South Texas is in this sense a microcosm of planetary patterns. While some regions, communities, and systems will benefit from a warmer world, most will not. However, *our region is also different.* This is not the American midwest or western Europe, areas of comparable size but better situated for a variety of reasons to deal with and adapt to climate change. Like the subarctic zone of Alaska, subtropical South Texas faces special challenges due to a combination of physical and human geography factors. Among these the following are noteworthy: rapid population growth; economic underdevelopment; unique but vulnerable ecology; significant but vulnerable agriculture; and limited water supplies. Then there are the three great overarching realities of coastal location, the existing semi-desert to subhumid climate, and, finally, the subtropical location itself.

The result of all this is a regional challenge which we believe is the greatest test South Texas has faced since its first human inhabitants arrived ten or so millennia ago. Our job was to describe and explain that challenge to the best of our ability. It is up to the present and next generation of citizens and leaders to "come and take it." We are confident that they, you, will do so.

Thank you for your interest and attention. *Vaya con Dios.*

Subject Index

A

accretion, 92, 62, 66

aerosols, 7,8,9,69,92,97

air pollution, 45, 92, 93, 96, 97, 101

air quality, 45, 69, 91, 92, 93, 96, 97, 98, 103, 104

albedo, 43

algorithms, 6, 116

amphibians, 80, 81

anomalous, 18

anthropogenic, 7, 8, 9, 17, 21, 53, 54, 69, 81, 92, 97, 104, 111, 112, 121, 127

agriculture sector, 130, 131

assessment, 8, 9, 42, 44, 45, 53, 92, 112, 119, 147, 149, 150, 151

atmosphere, 5, 6, 7, 8, 15, 17, 43, 44, 45, 92, 93, 97, 104, 112, 116, 118, 119, 121, 127

B

Baffin Bay, 57, 58, 59

bat, 82

birds, 81, 82, 84, 85, 133, 134, 135, 136, 138, 139, 140, 142

Blanco Creek, 113

bobwhite, 83, 85

brackish water, 57, 71, 73, 131

barrier islands, 57, 60, 61, 65, 66, 71

brush, 17, 82, 85, 119

C

C4 grasses, 79, 82, 85, 86

CAMS, 100

CAMX, 98

Canada, 11, 16

Chihuahuan, 37, 134, 135, 137, 142

climate change, 5, 6, 7, 8, 9, 16, 19, 42, 44, 45, 46, 57, 60, 67, 71, 73, 79, 80, 81, 82, 84, 85, 86, 91, 92, 97, 98, 103, 104, 109, 110, 111, 112, 115, 116, 117, 119, 121, 122, 127, 130, 131, 134, 140, 142,

climate drivers, 7

climate gradient, 66, 69

climatologies, 5

compliance grade monitoring, 100

computer modeling, 5

carbon dioxide, 5, 8, 43, 52, 91, 92, 97, 127

chlorofluorocarbon, 8

conceptual models, 57, 96, 97, 111

Corpus Christi, 20, 46, 52, 58, 61, 65, 67, 69, 71, 93, 94, 98, 99, 100, 101, 102

cubical cells, 6

D

depositional subenvironments, 61

deer, 17, 80, 82, 83, 84, 85

Dengue fever, 45

drought, 12, 23, 26, 27, 34, 37, 45, 57, 61, 79, 80, 81, 82, 84, 85, 148, 151, 109, 121

drought of record, 12

dry spell, 15, 42, 50, 51

E

Ecosystems, 5, 58, 92, 148, 149, 151

El Nino, 6, 12

eight-hour ozone, 91, 93, 94, 96, 97, 99, 100, 101, 102, 103

evaporation, 5, 11, 26, 58, 66, 71, 111, 112, 116, 118, 131

evapotranspiration (ET), 15, 19, 23, 26, 45, 109, 112, 115, 116, 117, 118, 119, 121, 127, 128, 138

emission, 8, 11, 42, 44, 45, 46, 50, 51, 60, 92, 93, 96, 97, 98, 99, 103, 104

155

energy balance, 5

erosion, 8, 59, 61, 69, 71, 131

estuarine, 57, 58, 60, 66, 67, 71, 73

event based models, 112

extinction event, 17

F
feedback mechanism, 6, 7, 8

G
geophysical, 9

glaciations, 8

glaciers, 5, 9, 44, 65, 80

global climate, 5, 6, 7, 8, 9, 44, 46, 60, 67, 80, 81, 85, 86, 92, 109, 110, 121

global warming, 9, 11, 15, 21, 26, 42, 44, 45, 50, 51, 52, 53, 60, 65, 92, 97, 98, 147, 148, 150, 151

greenhouse gas, 5, 6, 7, 8, 9, 42, 43, 44, 45, 46, 50, 61, 80, 92, 97

greenhouse effect, 43, 127

Guadalupe Estuary, 58, 66

Gulf of Mexico, 15, 17, 19, 34, 37, 58, 67, 112, 134

H
Hadley cell, 11

HEC-HMS, 112, 113

high ozone episode, 91, 93, 96, 97

Holocene, 45, 46, 60, 61

horizontal flow, 6

hurricane, 12, 16, 23, 42, 46, 79, 80, 84, 85, 97, 109, 148, 150, 151

hydrologic cycle, 11, 13, 127

hydrologic process, 109

hydrology, 16, 12, 112

hypoxia, 58

human volcano. 21

humidity, 12, 15, 19, 116, 127, 130

I
infectious diseases, 45, 46, 81

infrastructure, 148

Ingleside Barrier, 65

interannual variability, 37

intercontinental transport, 92, 103

Intergovernmental Panel on Climate Change (IPCC), 8, 9, 12, 42, 44, 45, 50, 60, 65, 80, 84, 91, 92, 97, 99

Inundation, 59, 61, 66, 67, 71, 121

L
land subsidence, 60, 61

latitudinal gradient, 67

Little Ice Age, 16, 21

littoral zone, 59

M
malaria, 45, 46

mammal, 17, 80, 82, 85

mangrove, 71, 73

mean annual precipitation, 15, 16, 23, 34, 42, 66, 84

mean annual temperature, 15, 19, 26, 46, 140

mean precipitation, 37, 50

mean summer temperature, 23

mean winter temperature, 23

Medio Creek, 111, 112, 113, 115, 121

megathermal, 18

meteorological, 8, 9, 83, 92, 94, 96, 97, 98, 99, 103

midden, 73

Mission River, 109, 111, 112, 113, 115, 121

model, 6, 7, 11, 12, 44, 45, 46, 50, 58, 61, 71, 91, 92, 96, 97, 98, 99, 100, 104, 109, 110, 111, 112, 113, 114, 115, 116, 117, 118, 119, 121, 122, 127, 128, 130, 131

mule deer, 82

Mustang Plains, 17

Mustang Island, 60, 61

N
National Ambient Air Quality Standards (NAAQS), 92, 94, 103

National Academy of Sciences (NAS). 8, 9, 42

National Center for Atmospheric Research (NCAR), 15, 17, 48, 98, 127, 128, 129, 130, 131

Near Non-Attainment (NNA), 98, 100, 101, 102
neotropical, 18, 134

non-attainment, 93, 96, 98, 103

NOx (nitrogen-oxygen compound), 92, 102

Nueces, 17, 57, 58, 60, 61, 65, 66, 61, 65, 66, 71, 73, 109

Nueces Delta, 57, 60, 61, 65, 66, 71, 73

Nueces Estuary, 58, 66

numerical model, 98

O
Oligohaline, 73

oyster reef, 58, 71

ozone, 45, 91, 92, 93, 94, 96, 97, 98, 99, 100, 100, 101, 102, 103

P
Pass Cavallo, 58

perturbation, 7, 91, 92, 97, 98, 99, 100, 101, 102, 103

photochemical modeling, 96, 98

photoperiod, 83

physiography, 58, 67, 134

potential evapotranspirationation, 15, 19, 23, 26, 109, 112, 118, 119, 128

Pleistocene, 15, 65, 66

precipitation, 5, 11, 12, 58, 66, 71, 109, 111, 112, 118, 121, 128, 130, 131

precipitation intensity index, 50

Preliminary Conceptual Model (PCM), 96

probabilistic, 6

physiographic, 17

Q
quail, 83, 84, 85, 86, 135

R
radiation, 5, 7, 43, 81, 127

rainfall, 15, 16, 19, 23, 26, 34, 37, 42, 45, 80, 81, 84, 85, 112, 115, 116, 117

Rangia cuneata, 73

recharge, 109, 112, 115, 116, 117, 118, 131

reptile, 79, 80, 81

research, 5, 8, 9, 12, 15, 44, 60, 69, 79, 83, 84, 86, 98, 111, 143

rhizophora mangle, 71

Rincon Bayou, 73

Rio Grande, 18, 46, 109, 110, 127, 128, 130, 135, 136, 137, 138, 139, 140, 149

S
Sabine-Neches Estuary, 58, 66, 67

San Antonio, 46, 52, 58, 66, 93, 94, 96, 98, 99, 100, 101, 102, 109, 118, 121

sensitivity simulation, 99

simulations, 9, 11, 12, 15, 98, 99, 115, 116, 121, 139, 130, 131

State Implementation Plans (SIP), 96

Stratosphere, 7, 17, 91

subsidence, 60, 61, 69

Southern Oscillation Index (SOI), 67, 68

synoptic, 92, 96, 97, 103

T
Tamaulipan, 17, 133, 134, 135, 139, 142

taxa, 133, 142

temperature amplification, 44, 104

Texas Coastal Ocean Observation Network (TCOON), 98

Thiessen polygon, 12, 112

Thornwaite model, 130

tipping point, 42

total dissolved solids (TDS), 110, 131

Trinity-San Jacinto Estuary, 58, 66, 67

Tropospheric, 91, 104

twenty-first century, 147, 150

U
Urbanization, 104, 110, 111, 112, 117, 118, 119,
    121, 127, 131

V
Variability, 9, 12, 67, 91, 92, 93, 94, 97, 103,
    109, 110

Victoria, 20, 22, 93, 98, 99, 100, 101, 136, 138

volcanic eruptions, 7, 44, 92

vulnerable people, 8, 9, 11, 148, 151

W
water budget, 52, 110, 111, 112, 118, 121, 122

water quality, 45, 31

white-tailed deer, 80, 82, 83, 84, 135

Wild Horse Desert, 17

World Meteorological Organization, 8